# If you love animals

Pass the time

**Alison Steven**

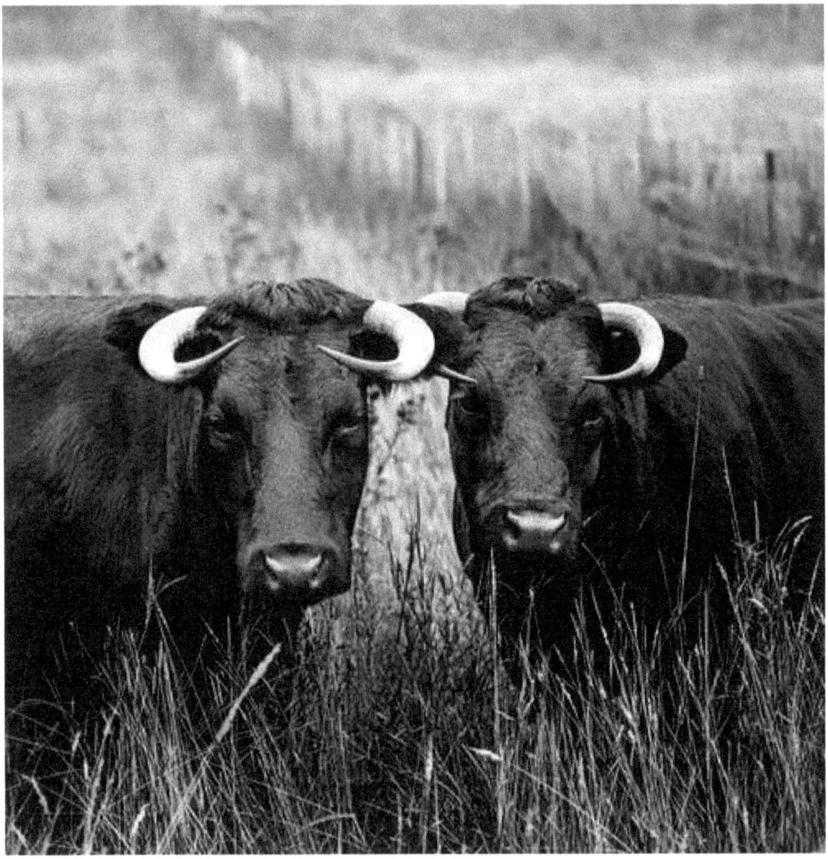

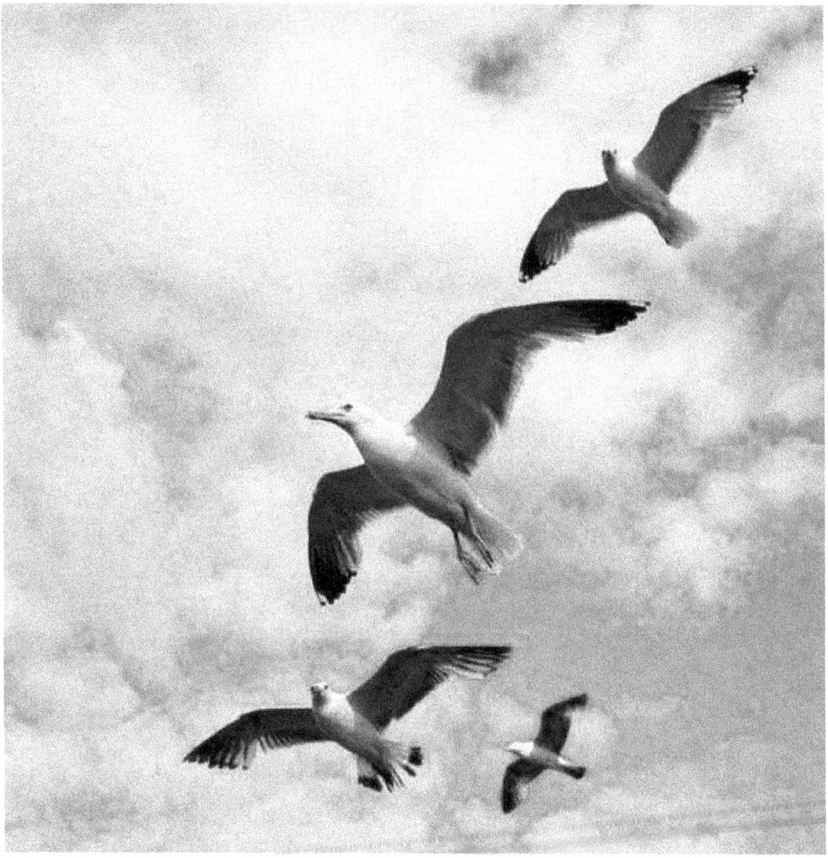

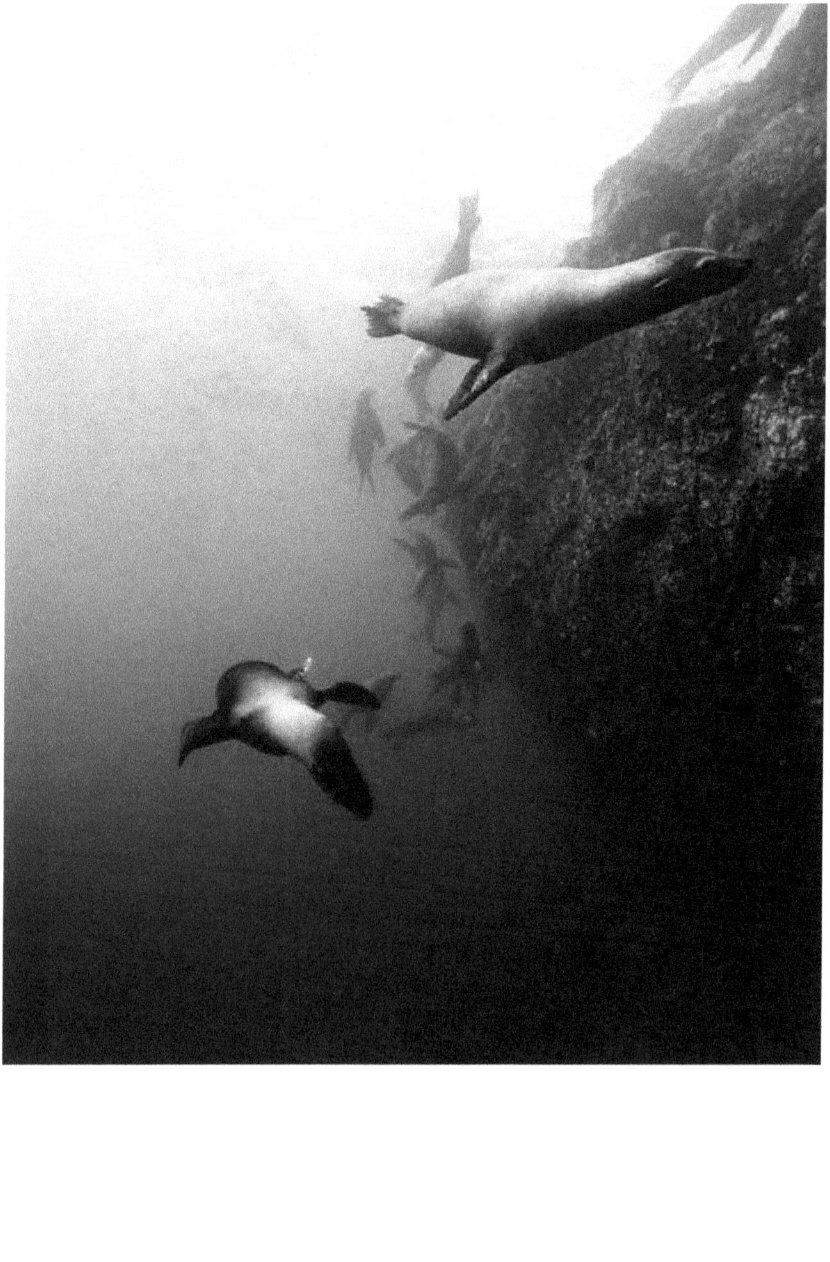

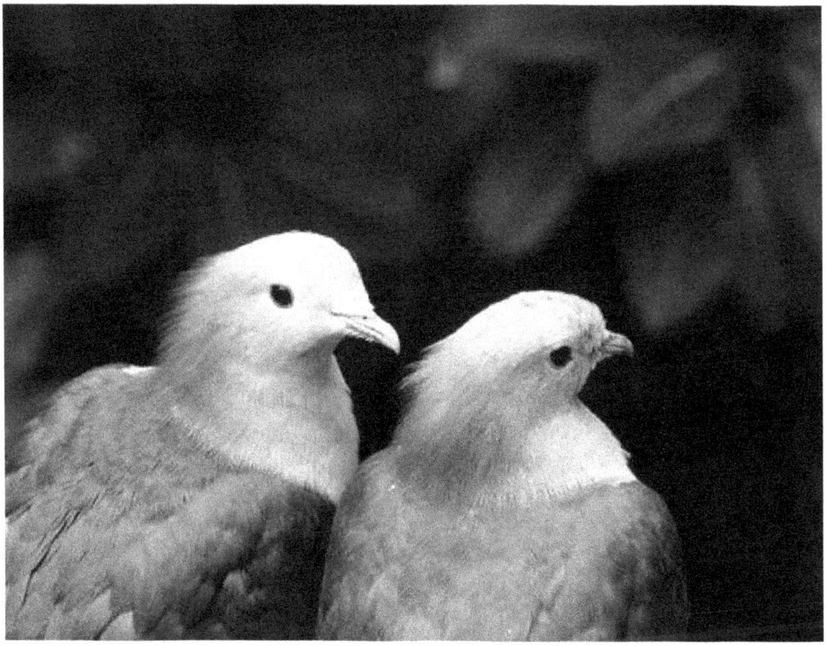

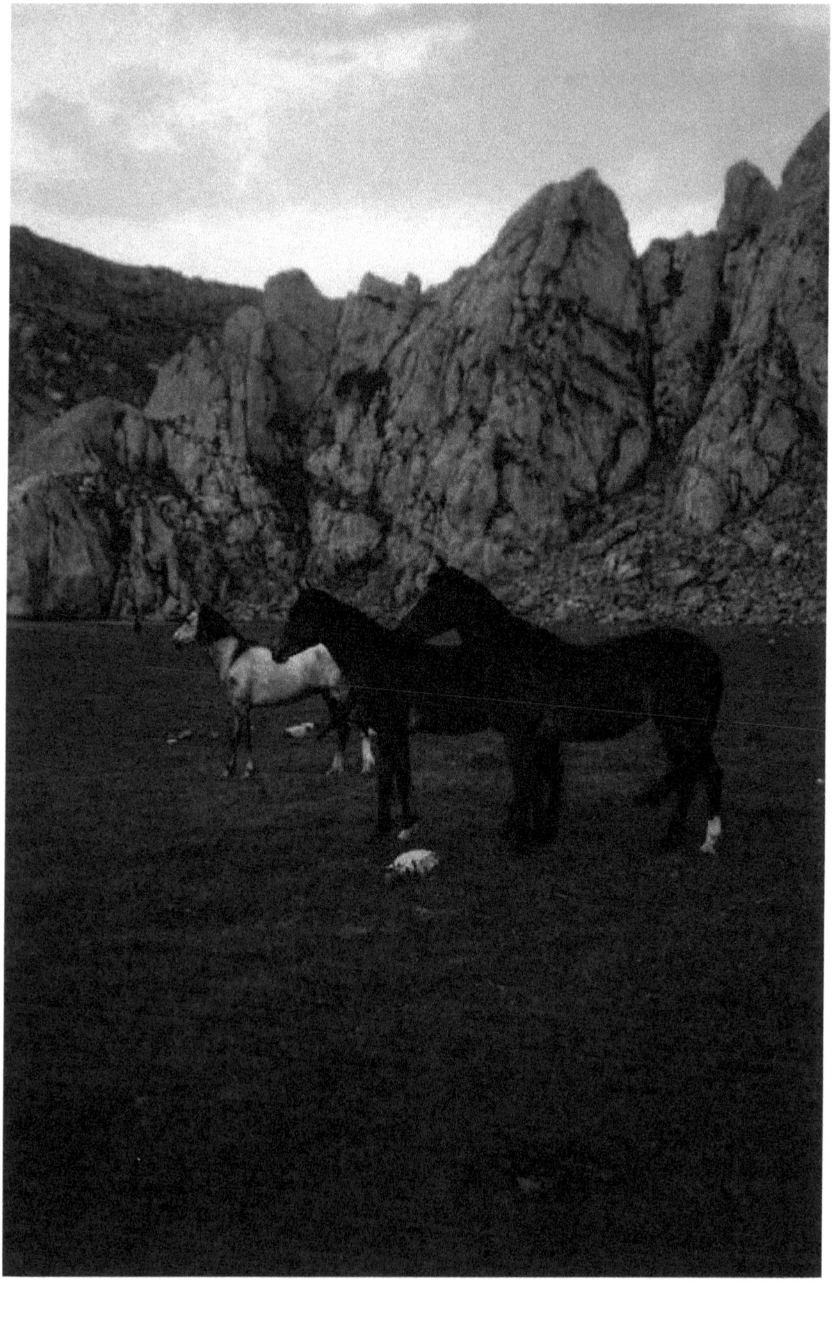

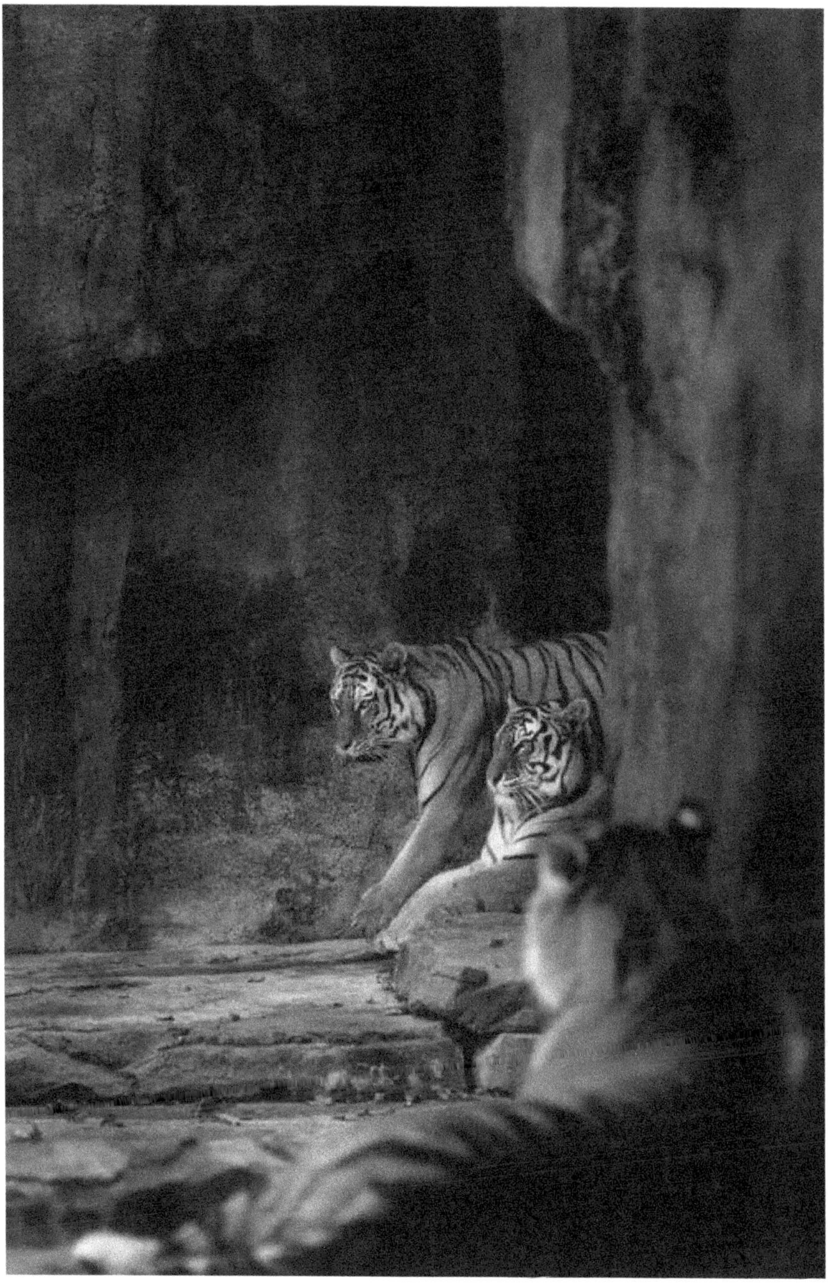

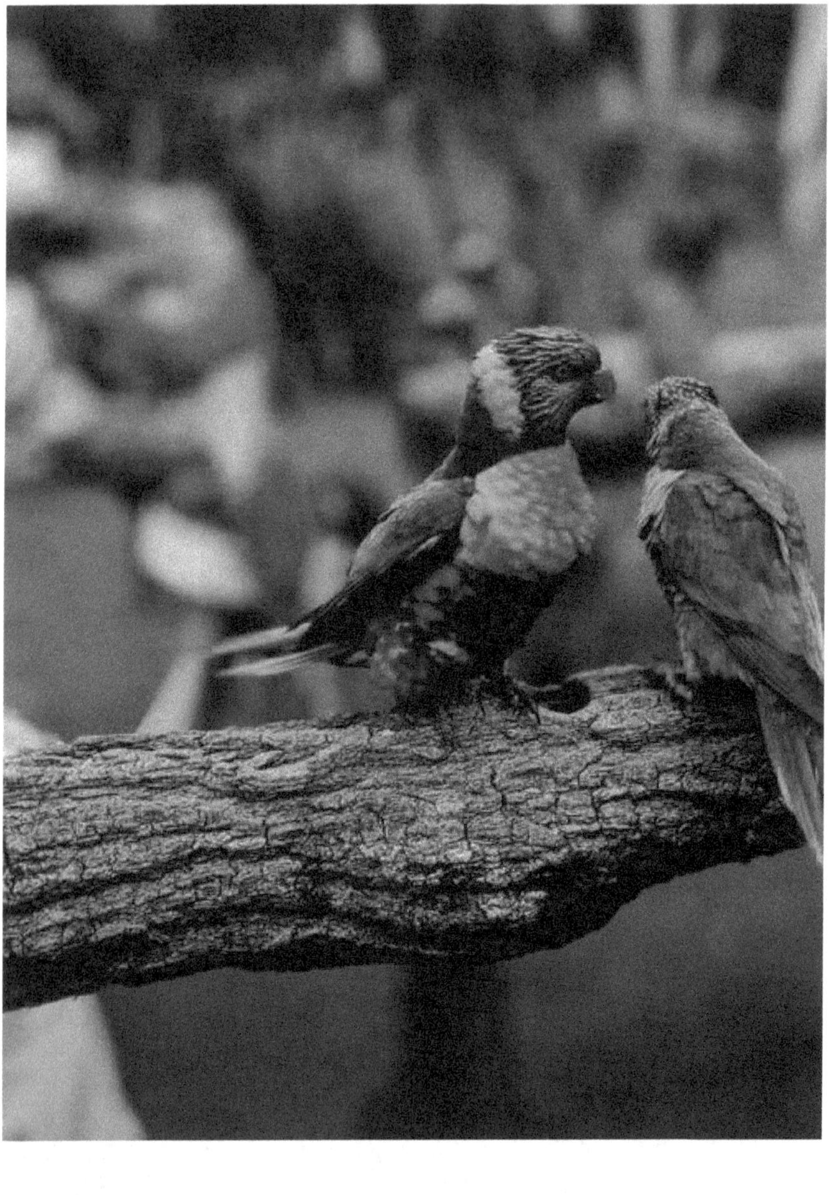

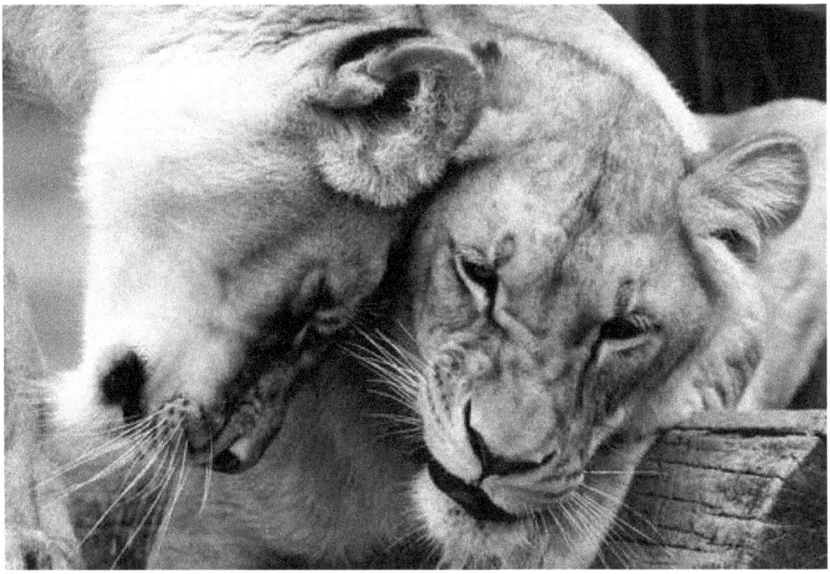

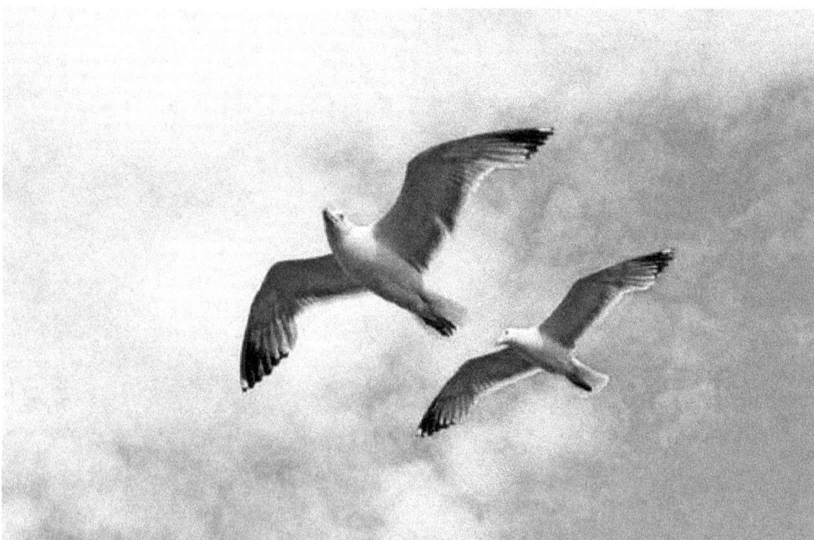

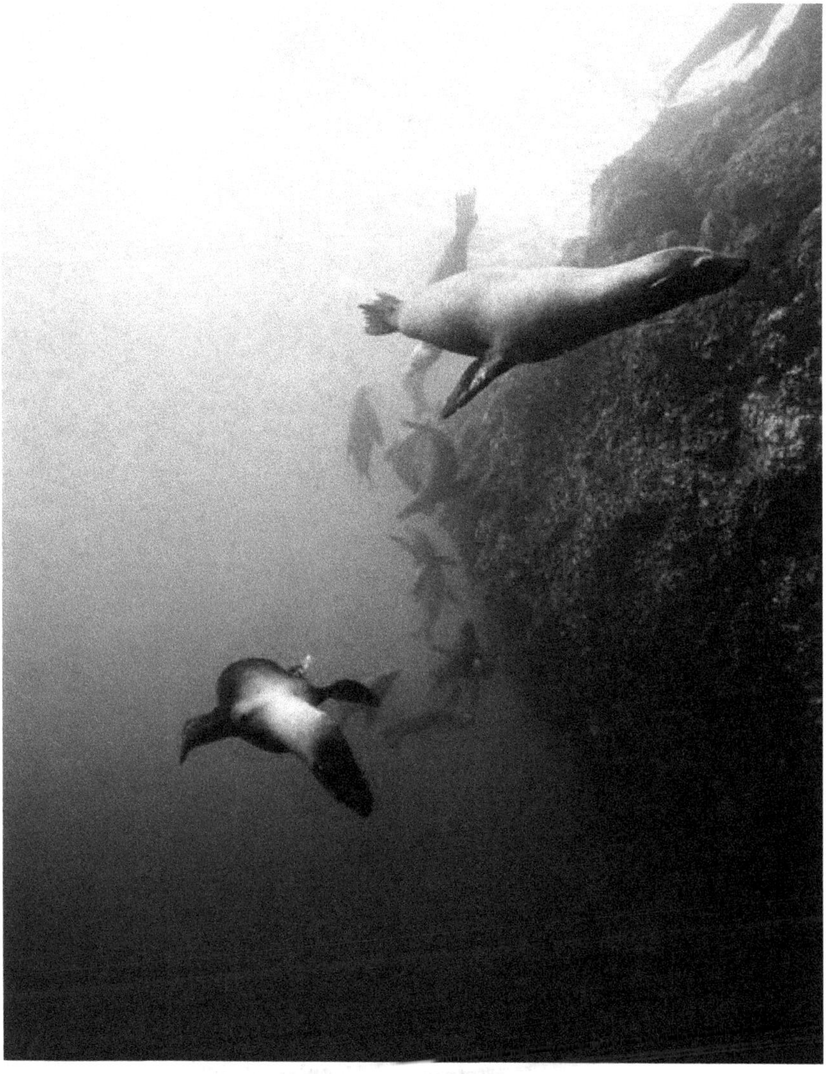

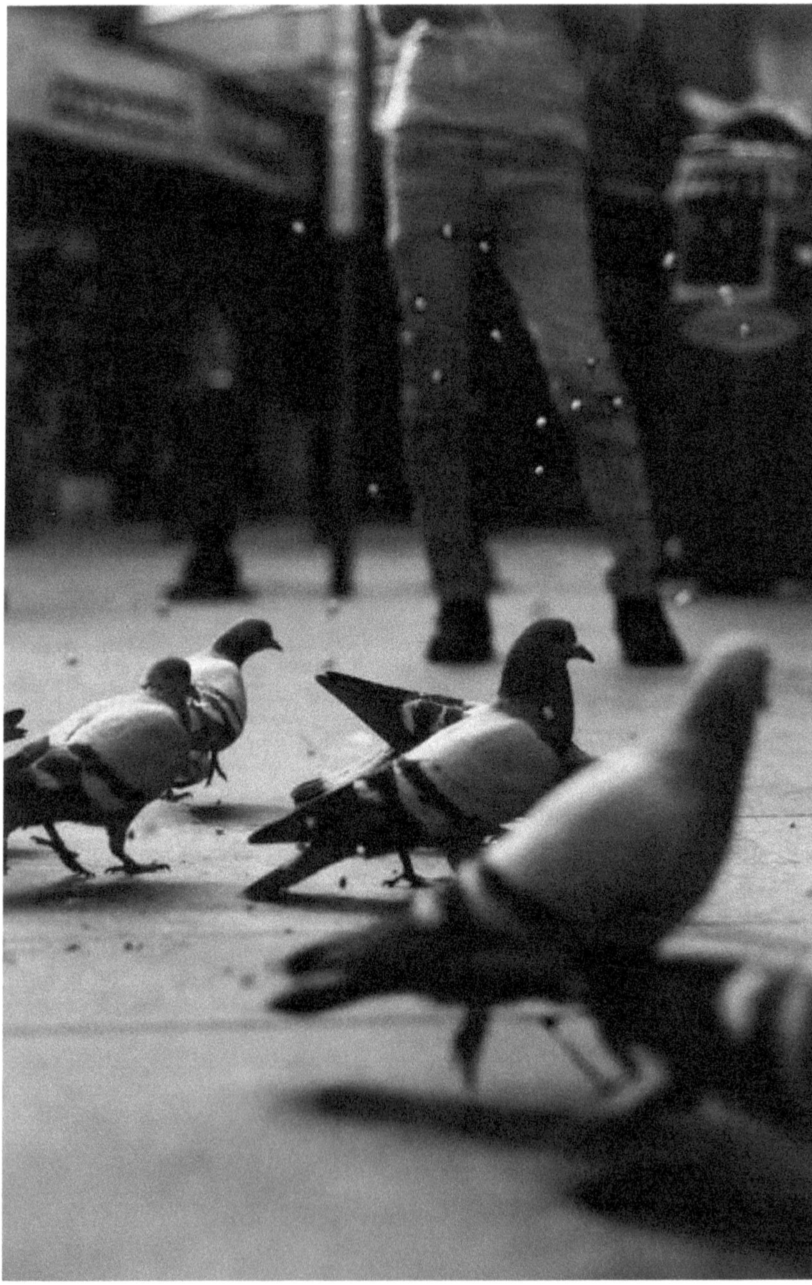

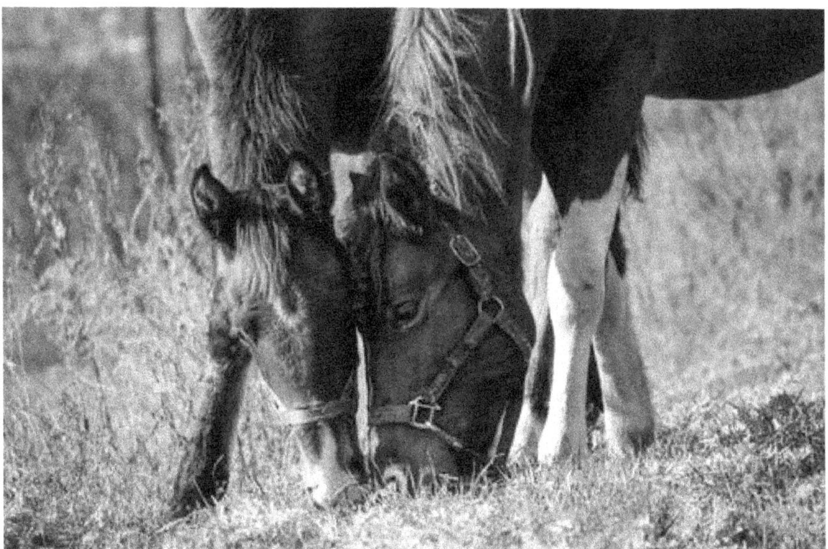

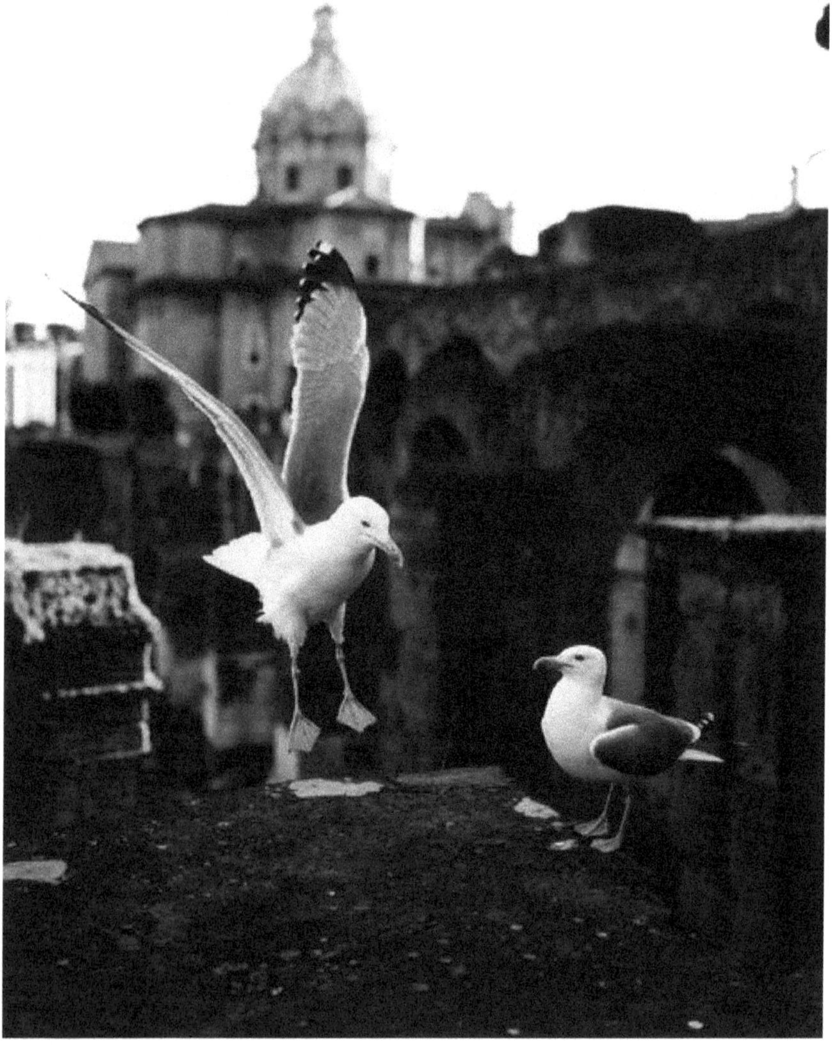

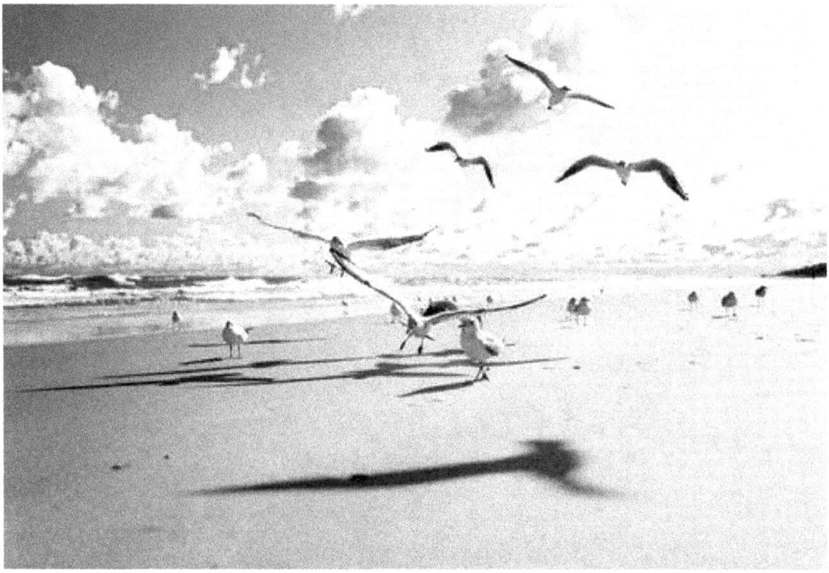

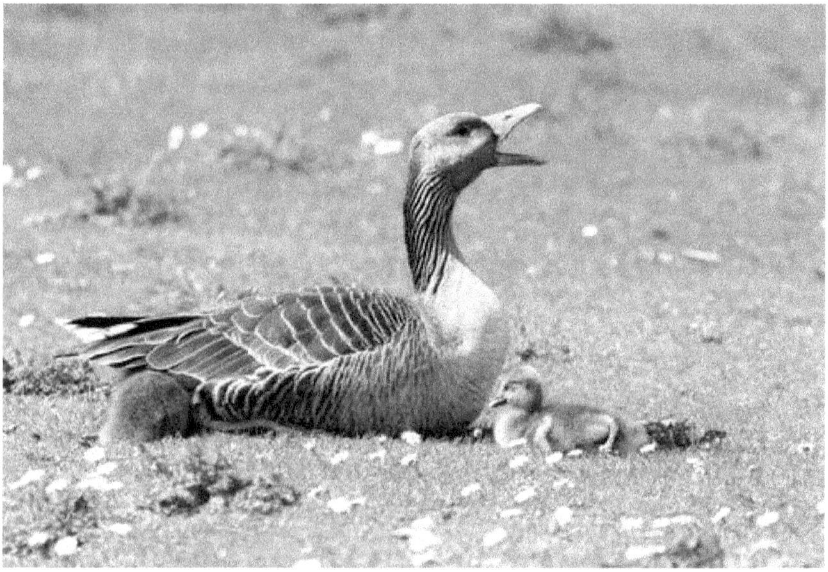

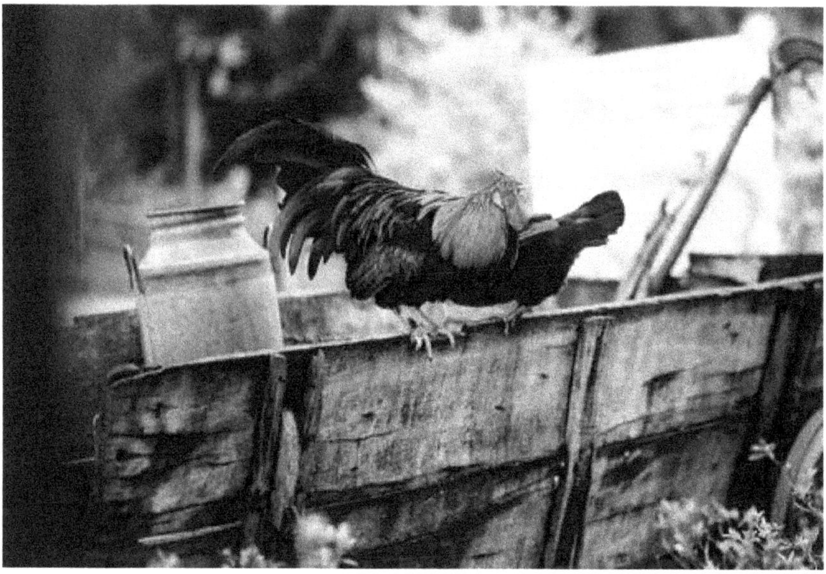

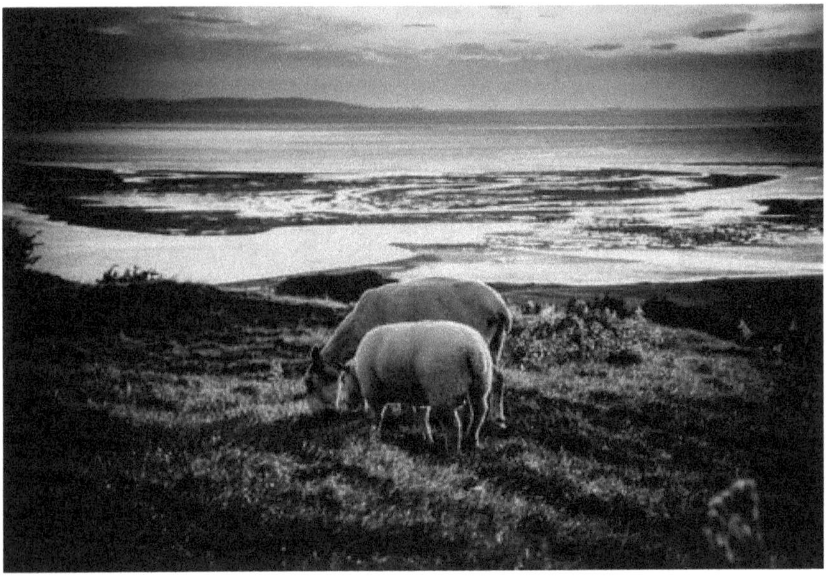

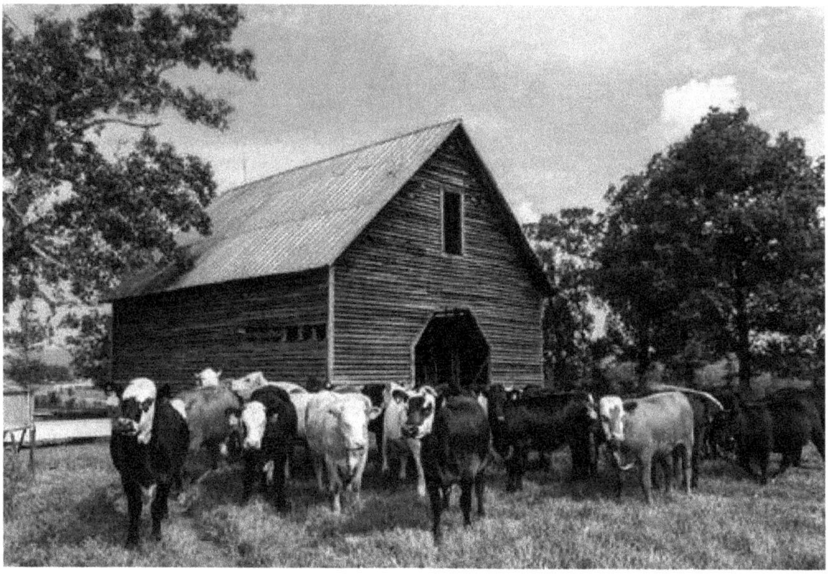

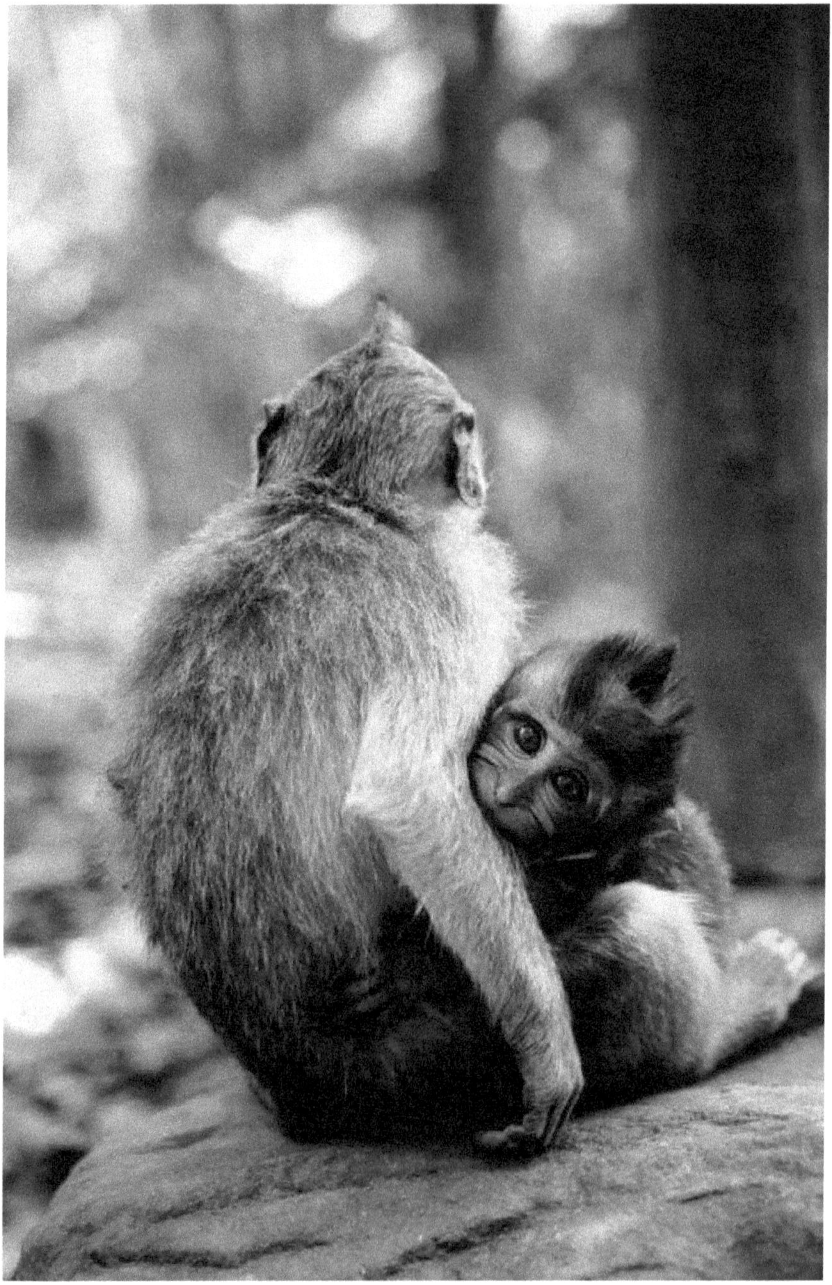

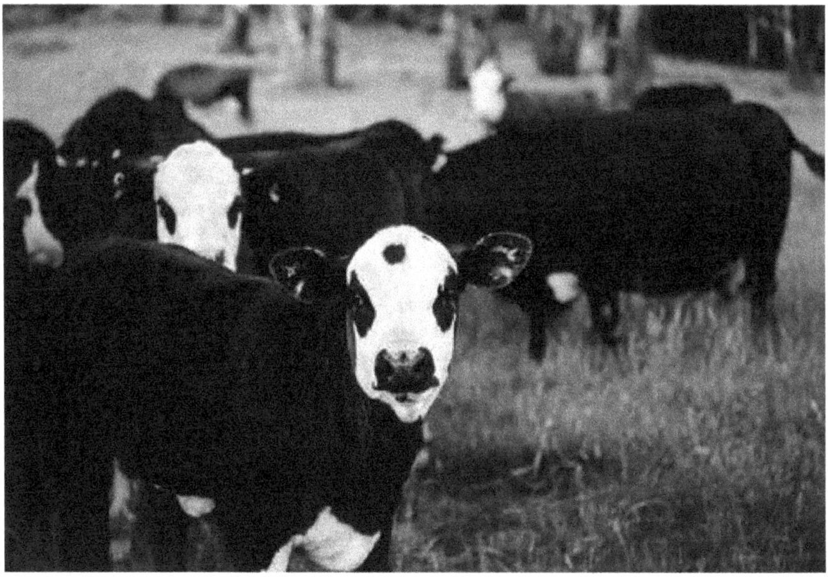

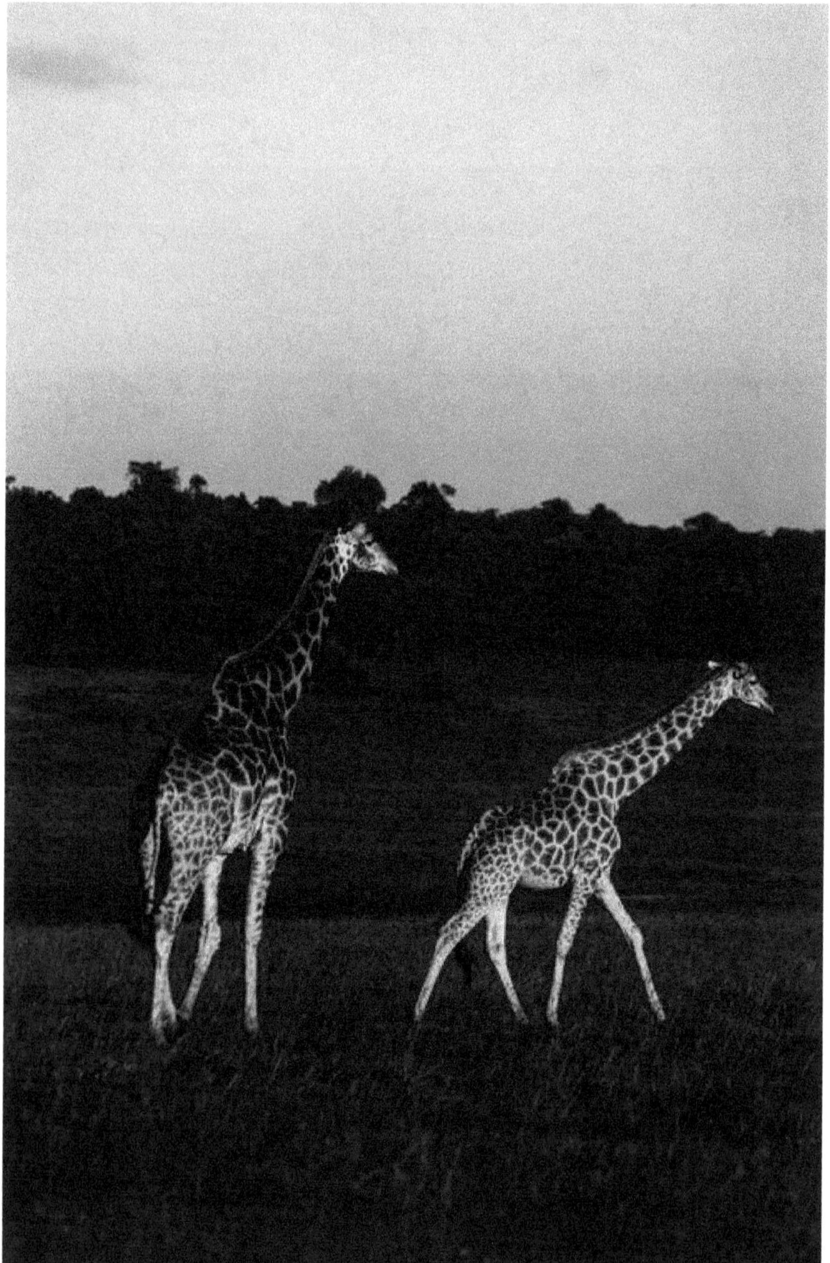

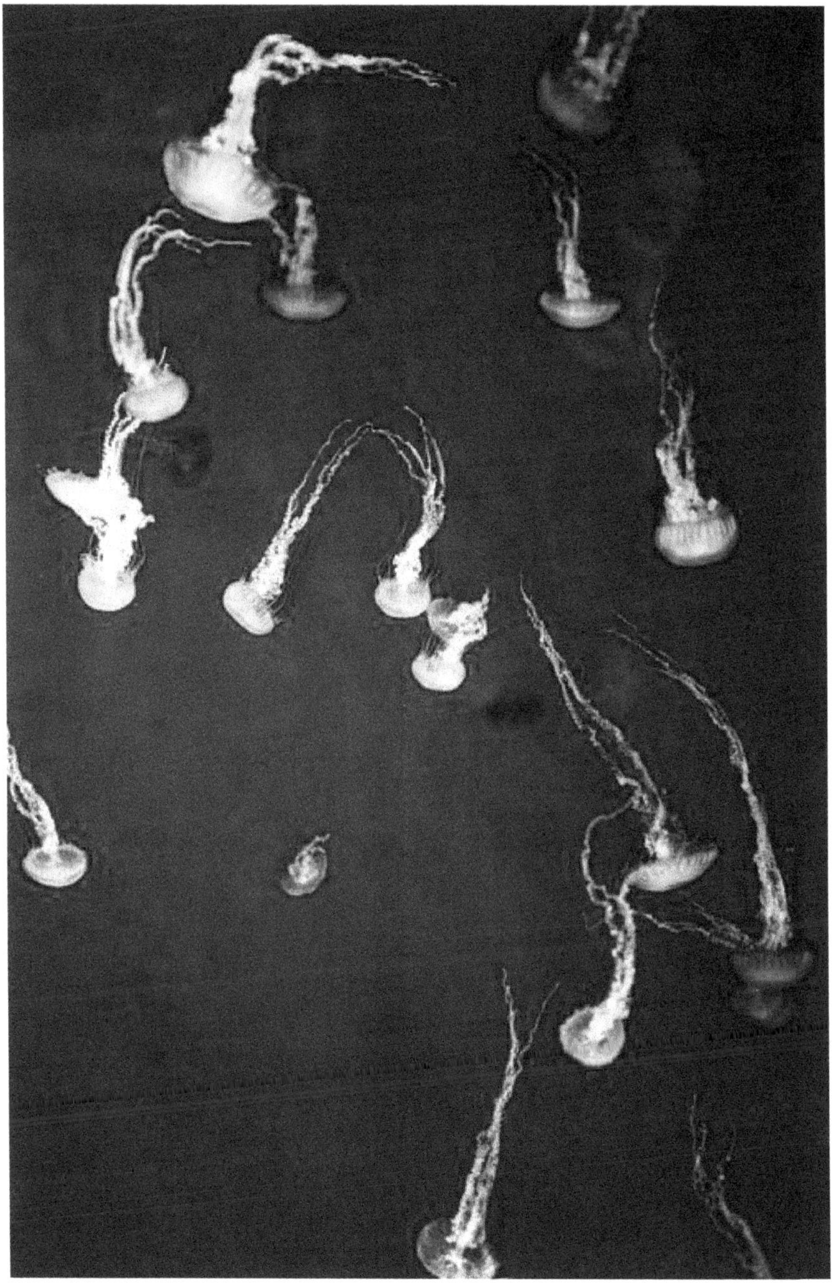

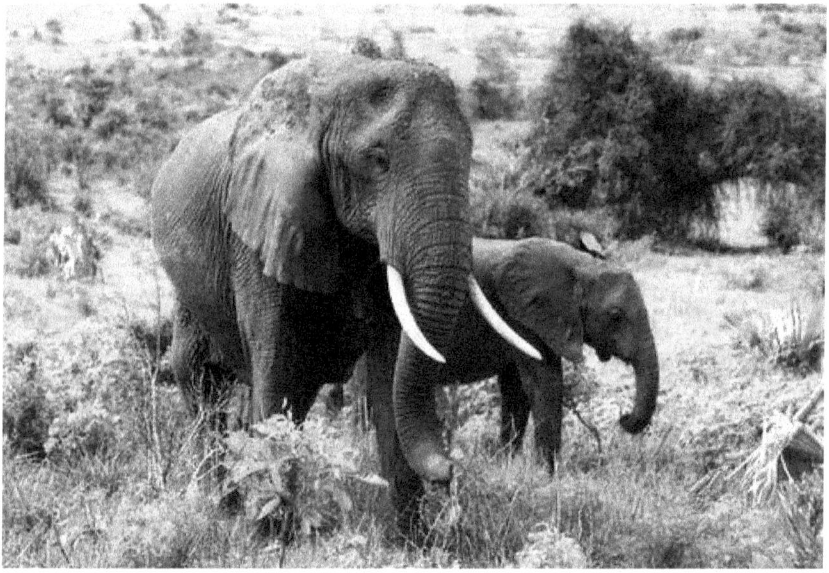

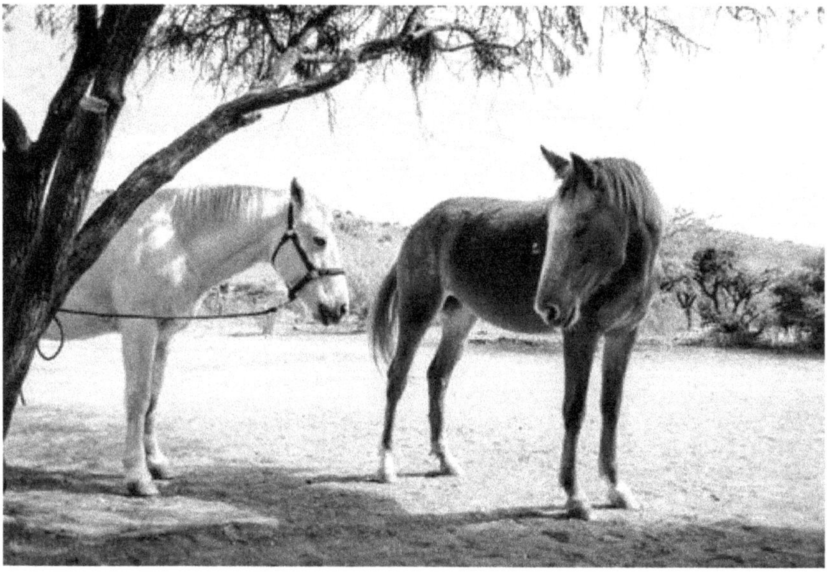

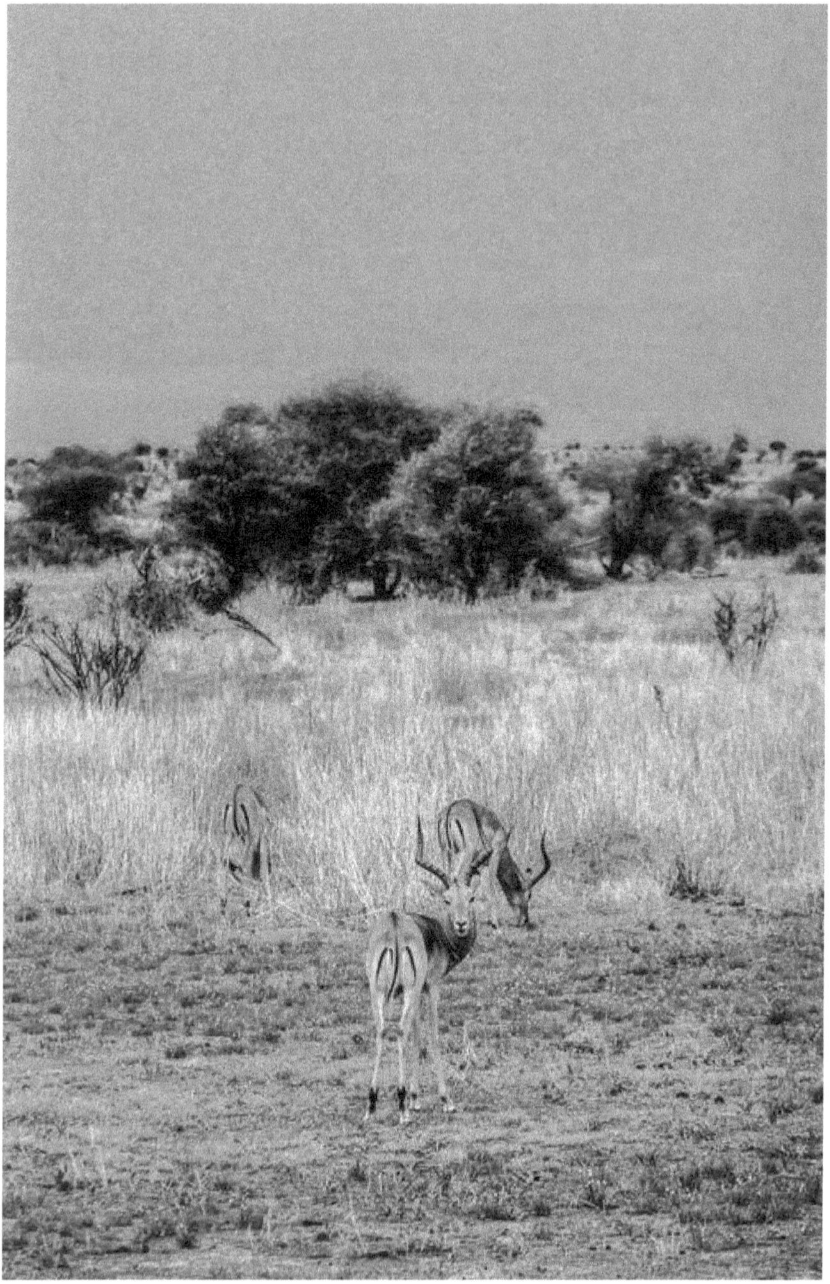

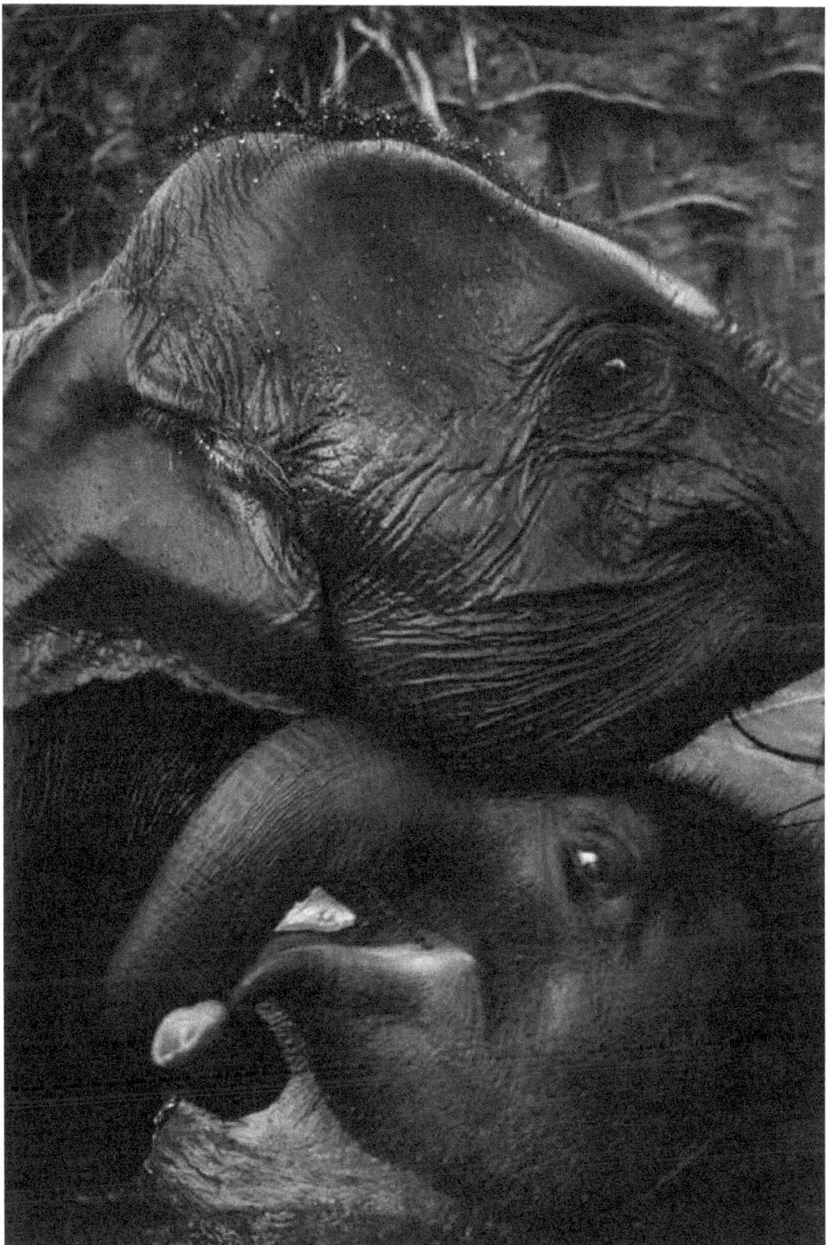

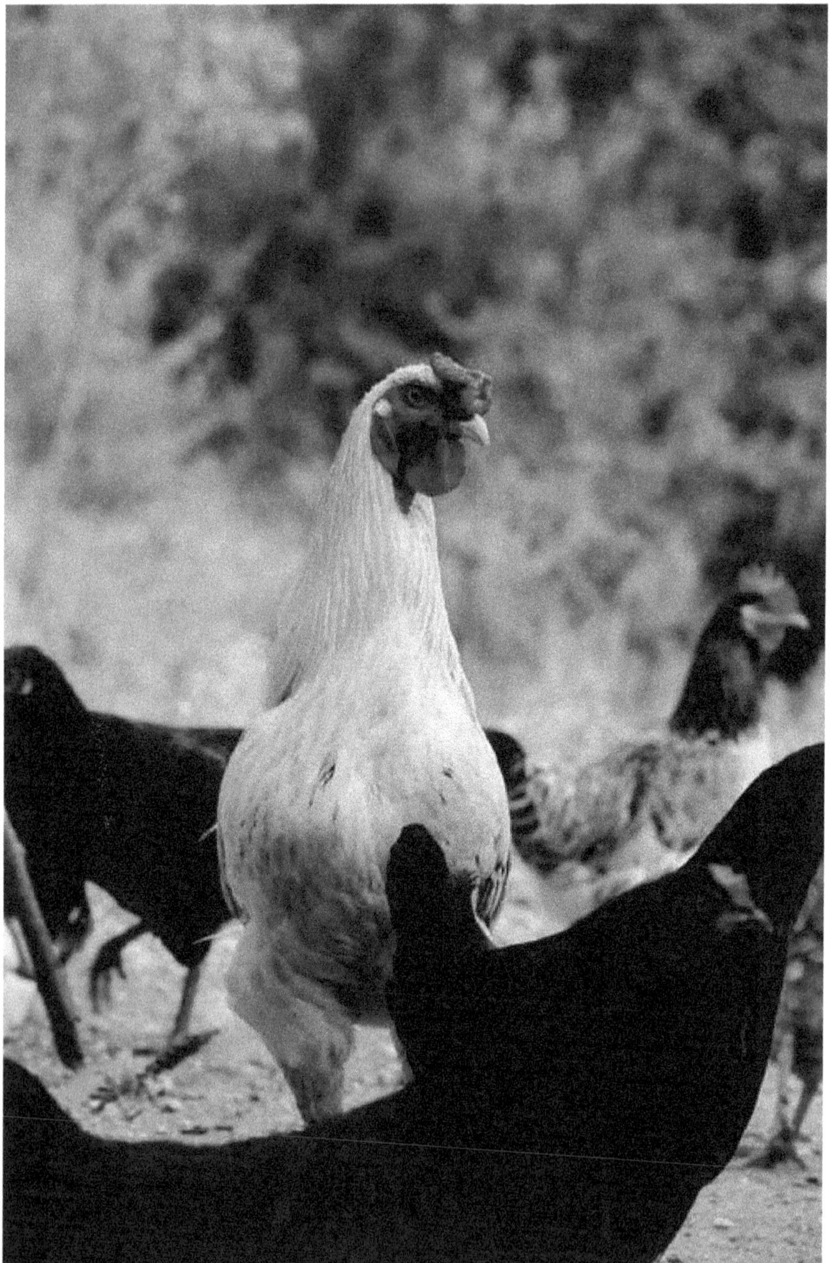

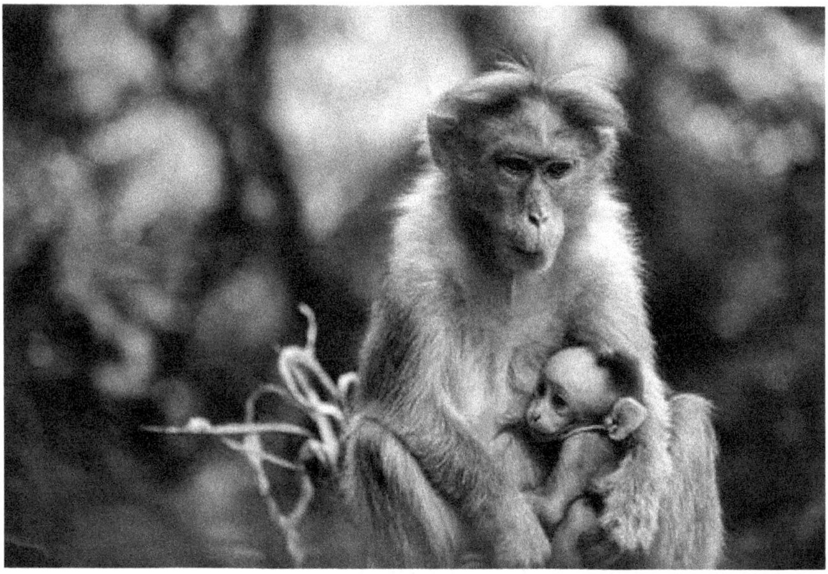

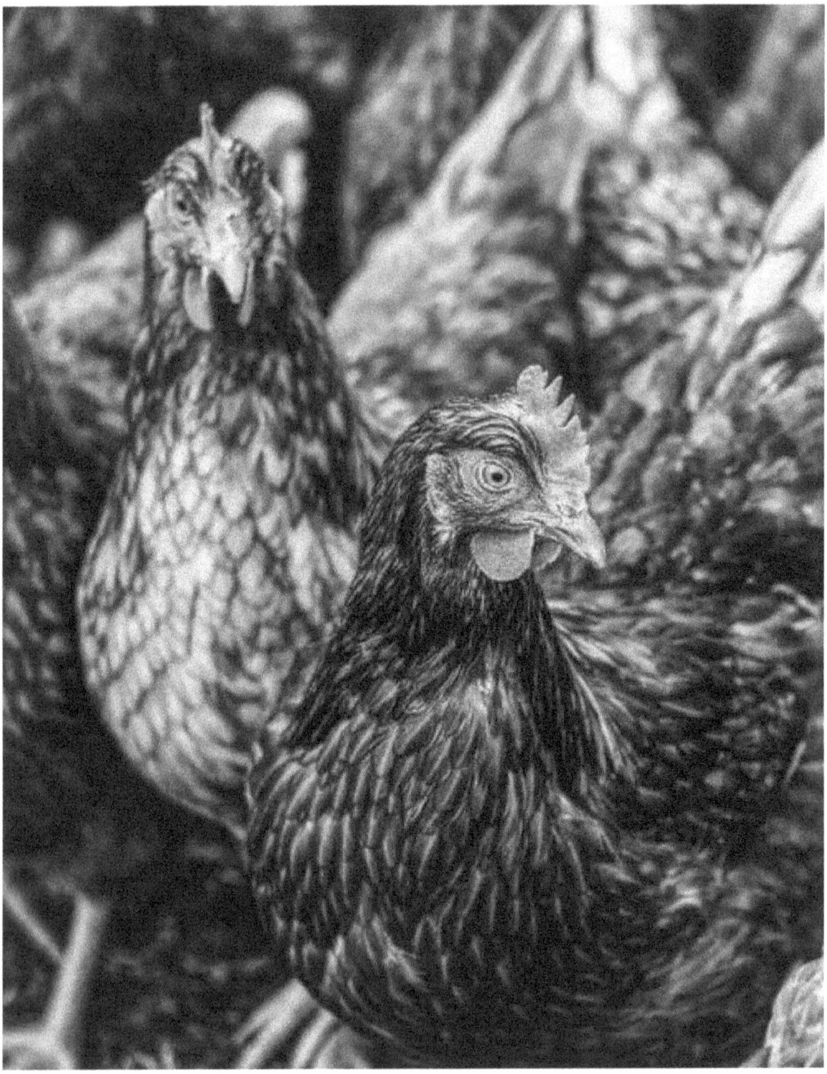

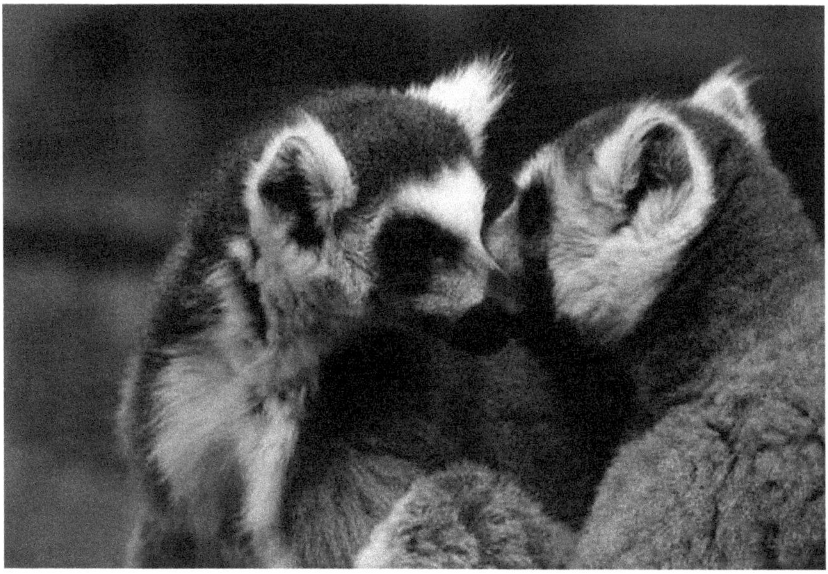

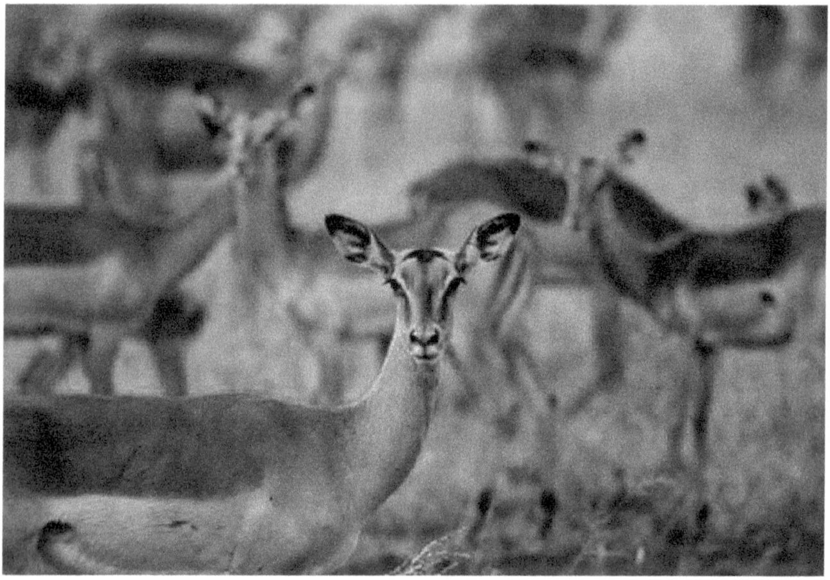

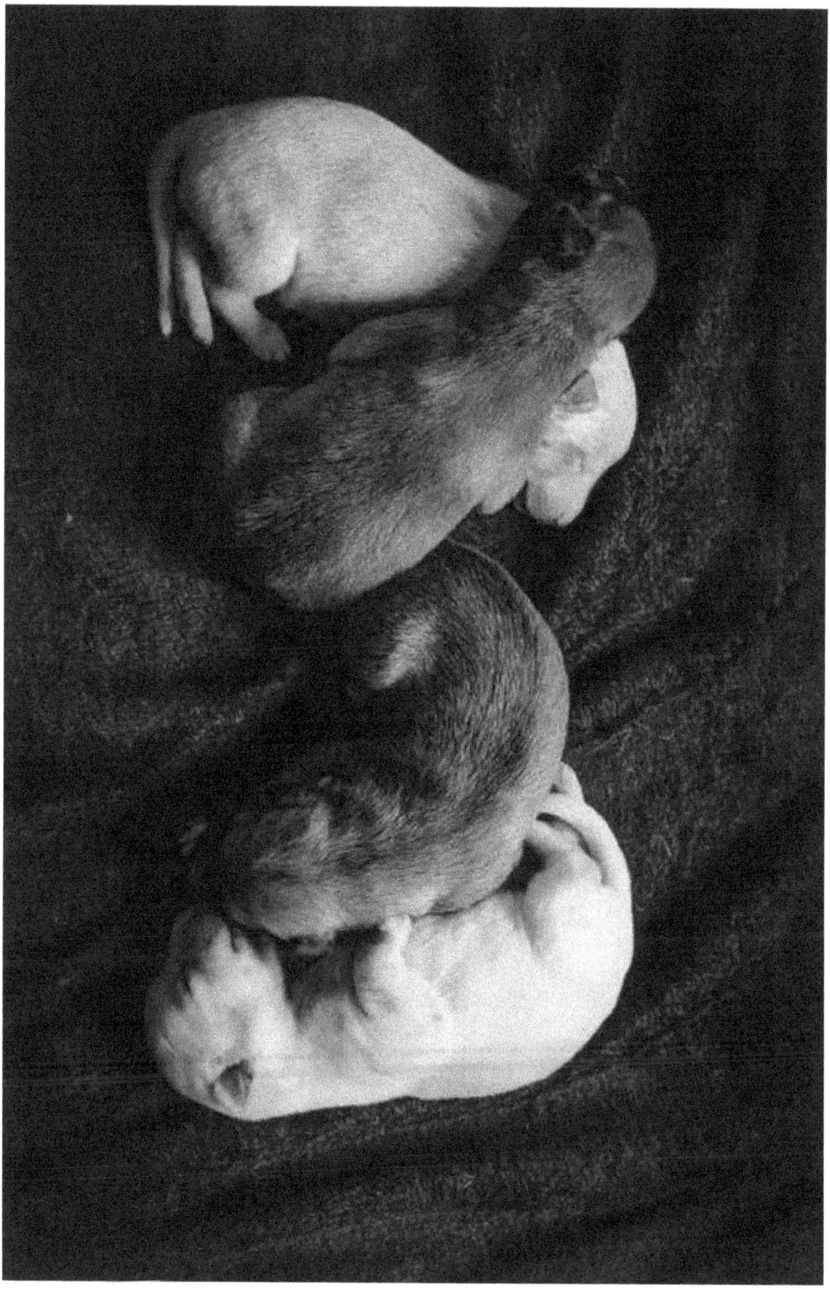

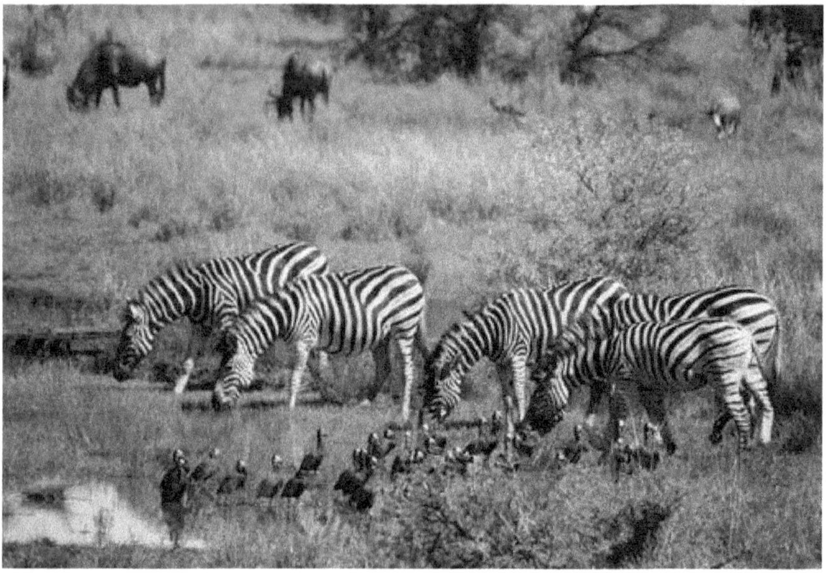

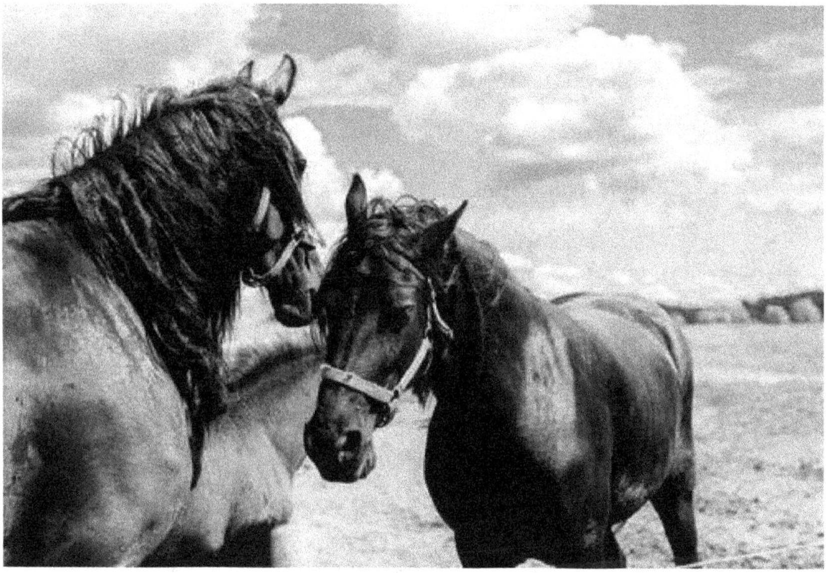

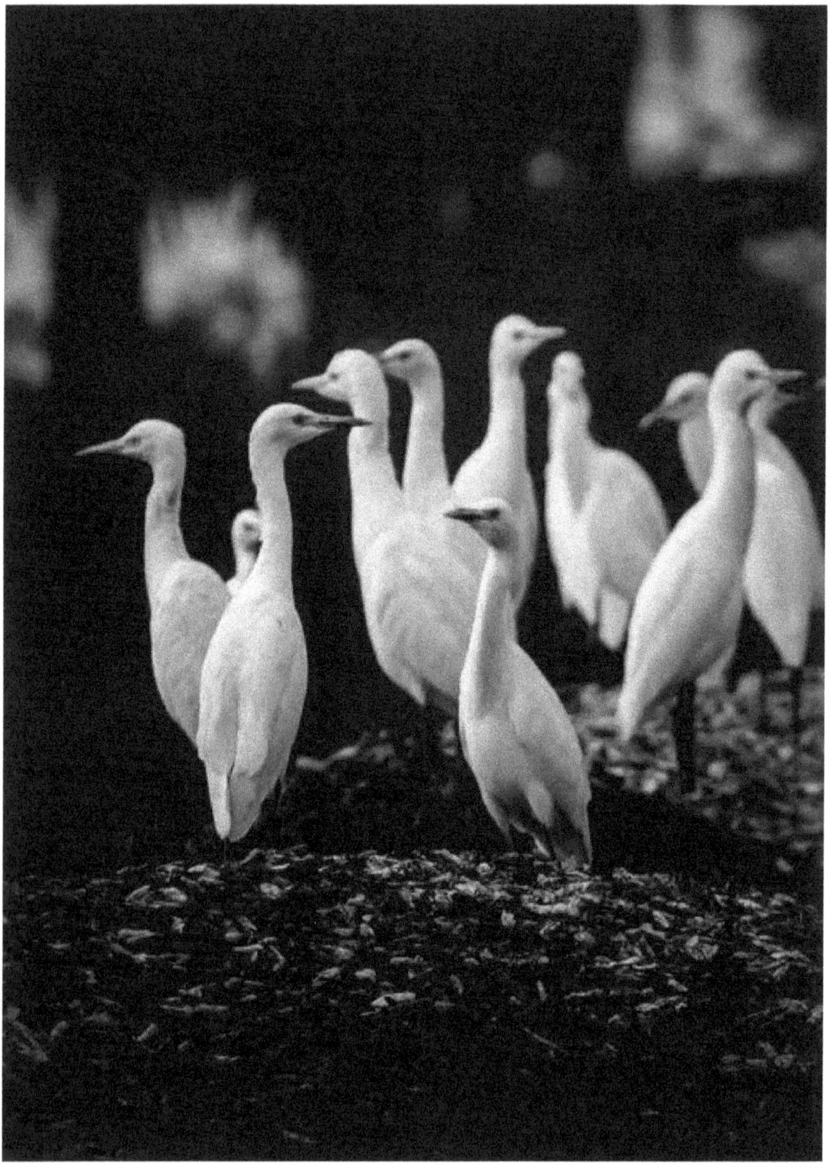

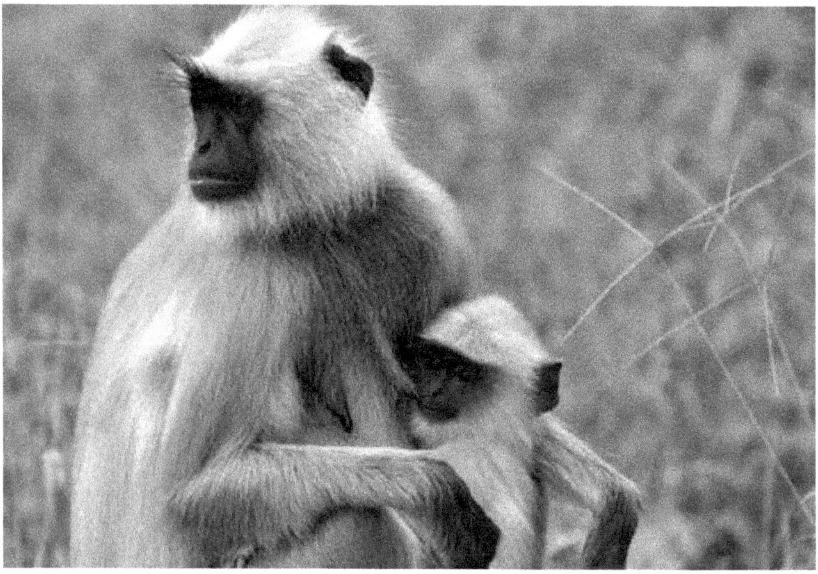

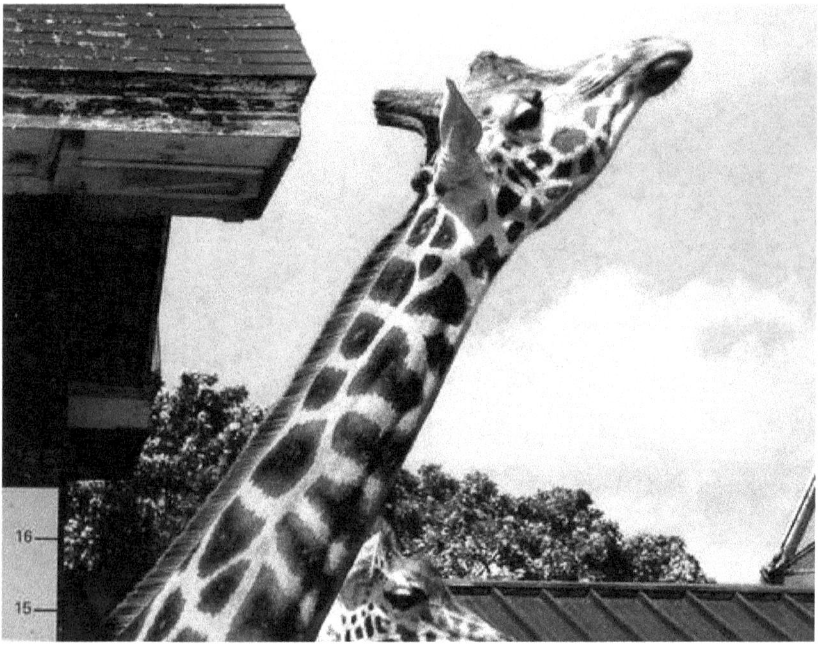
16
15

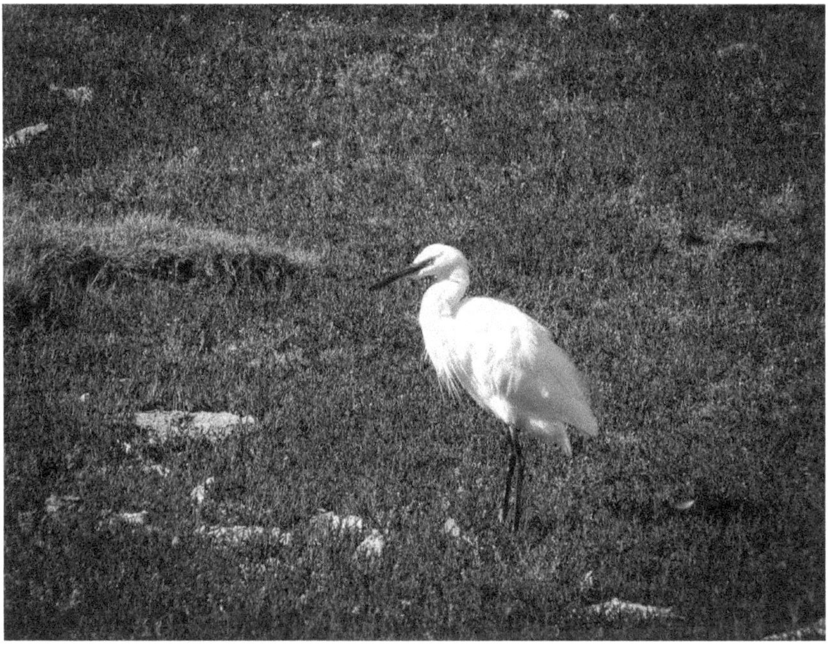

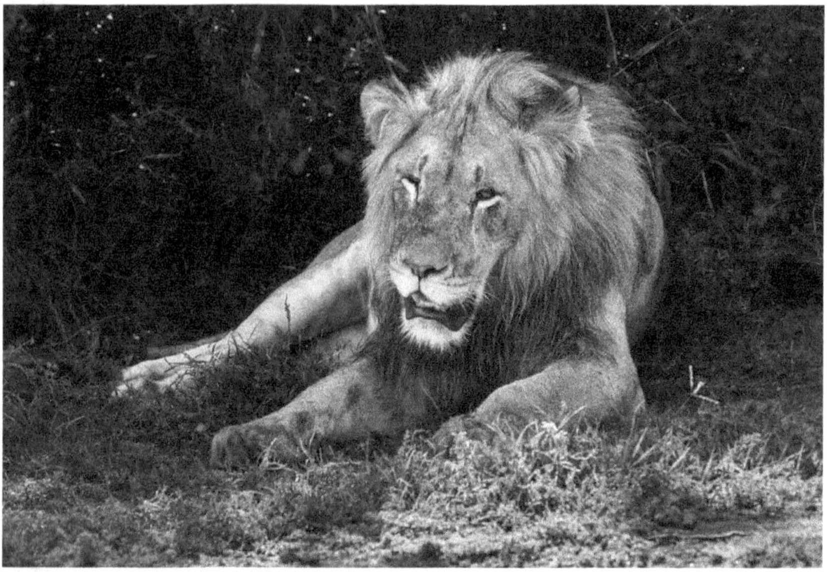

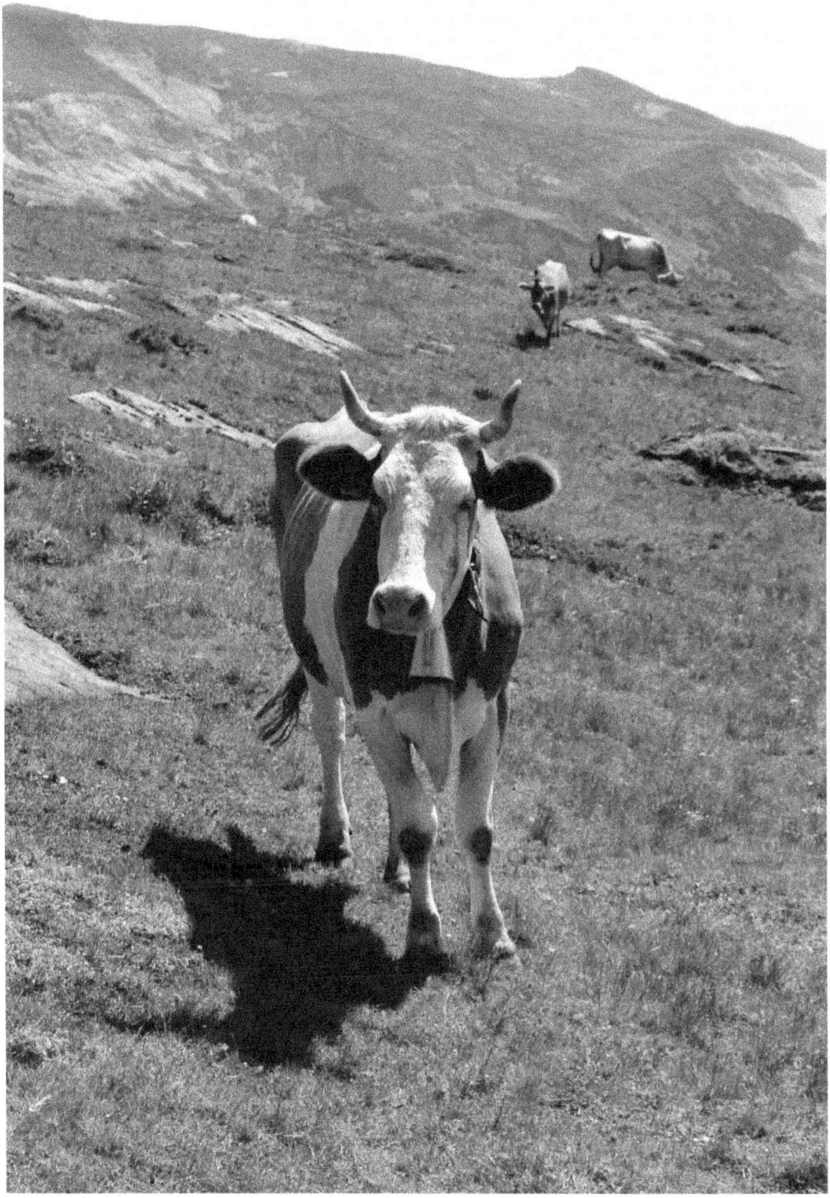

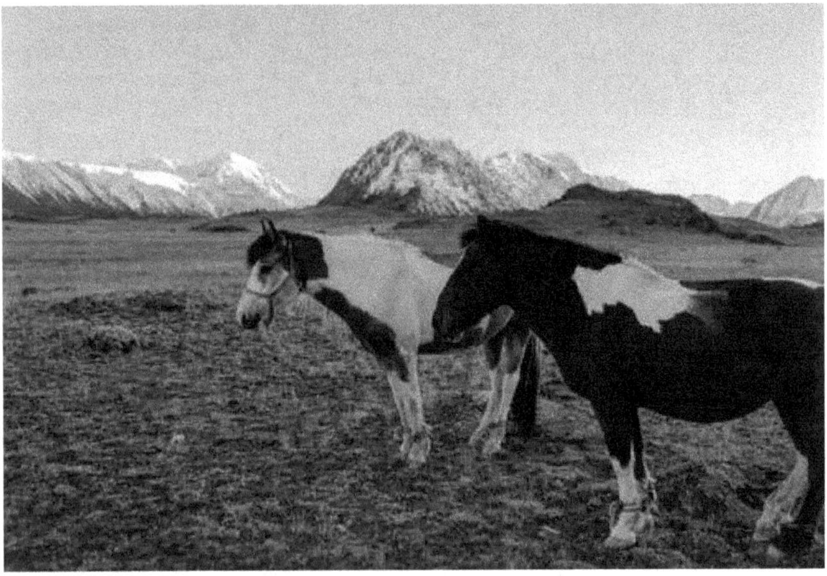

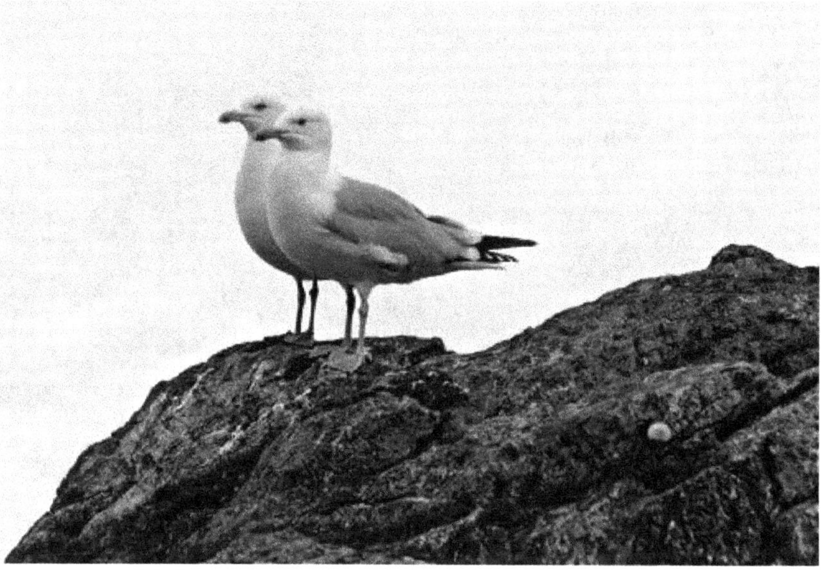

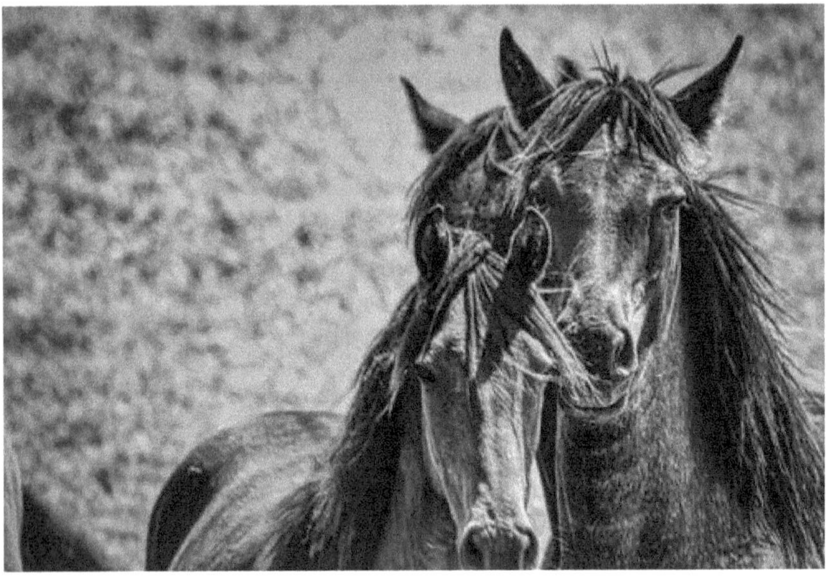

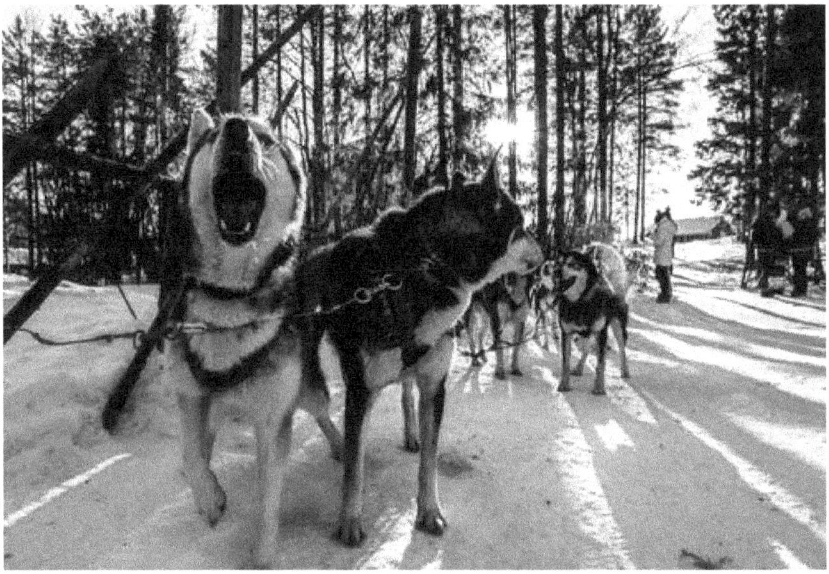

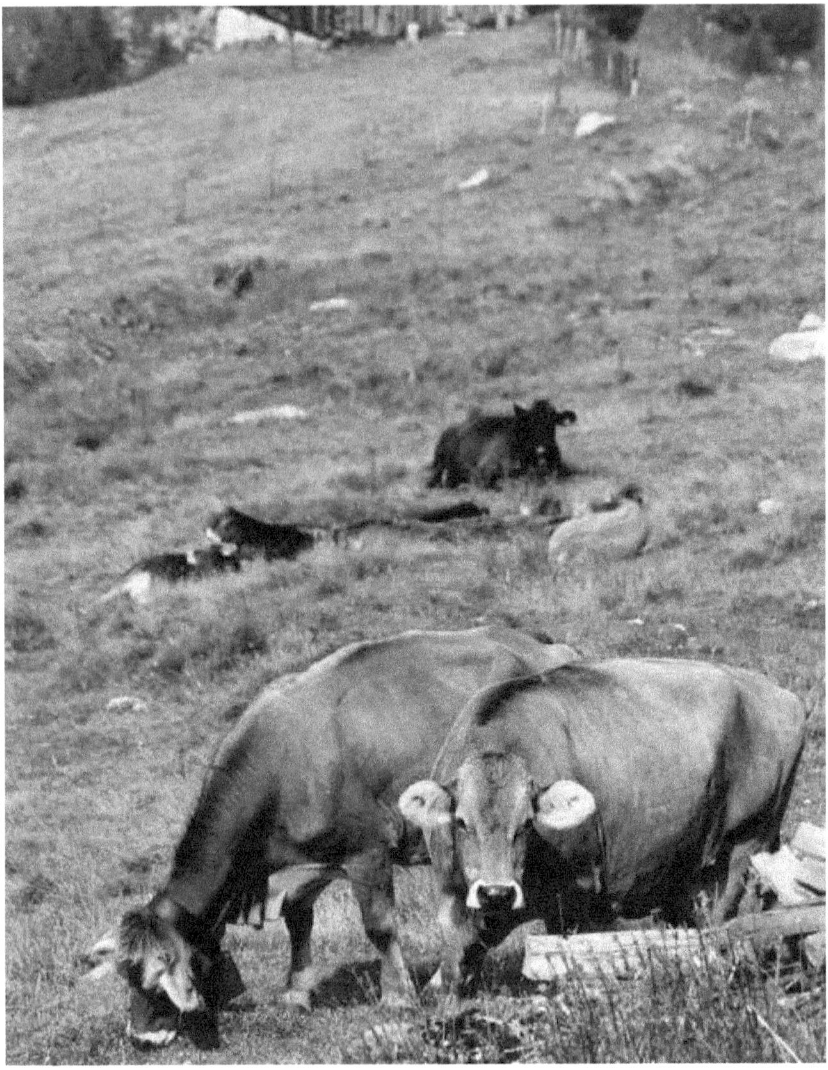

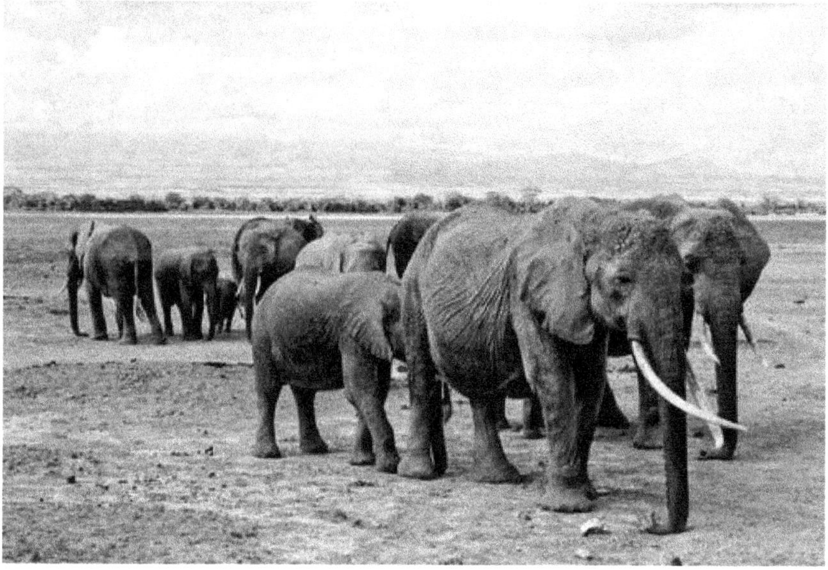

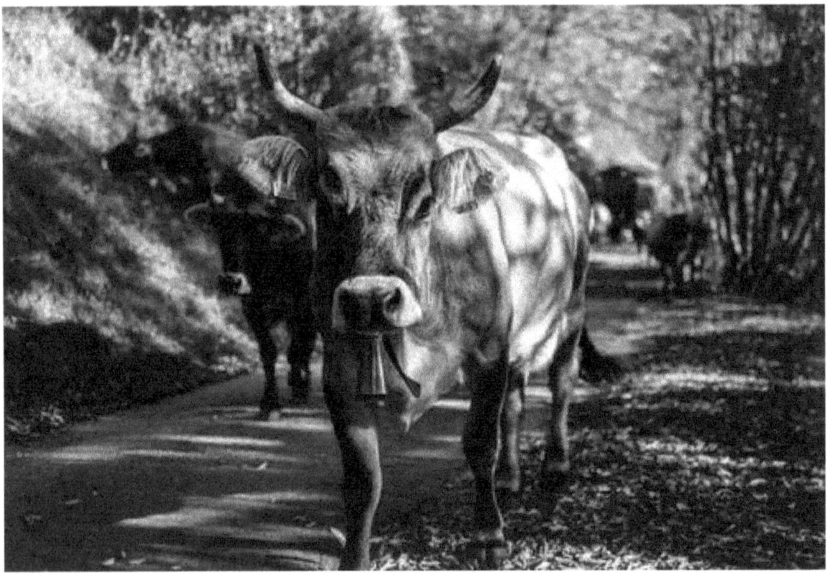

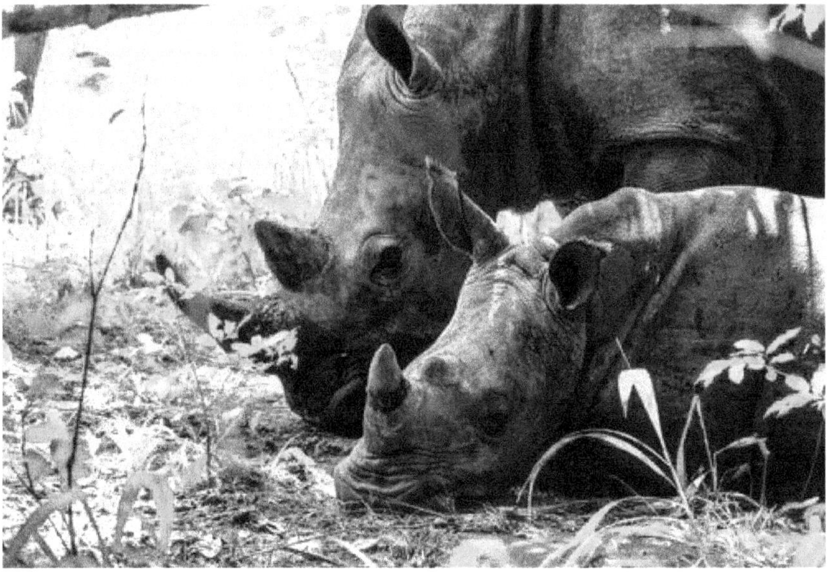

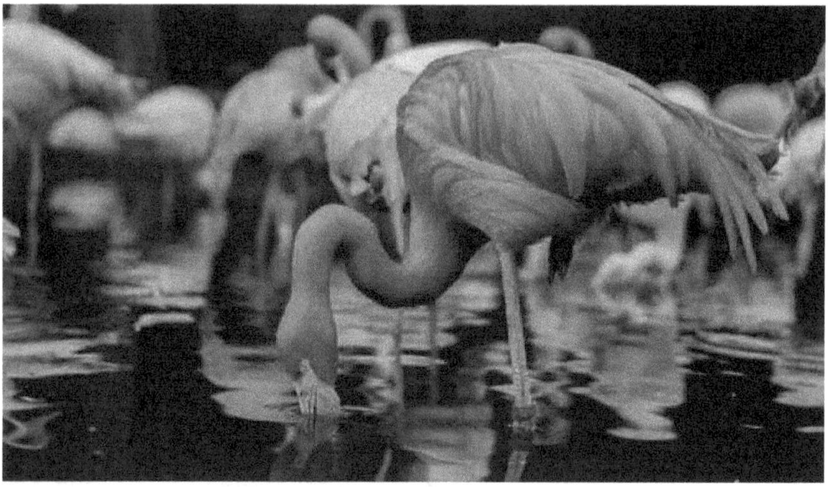

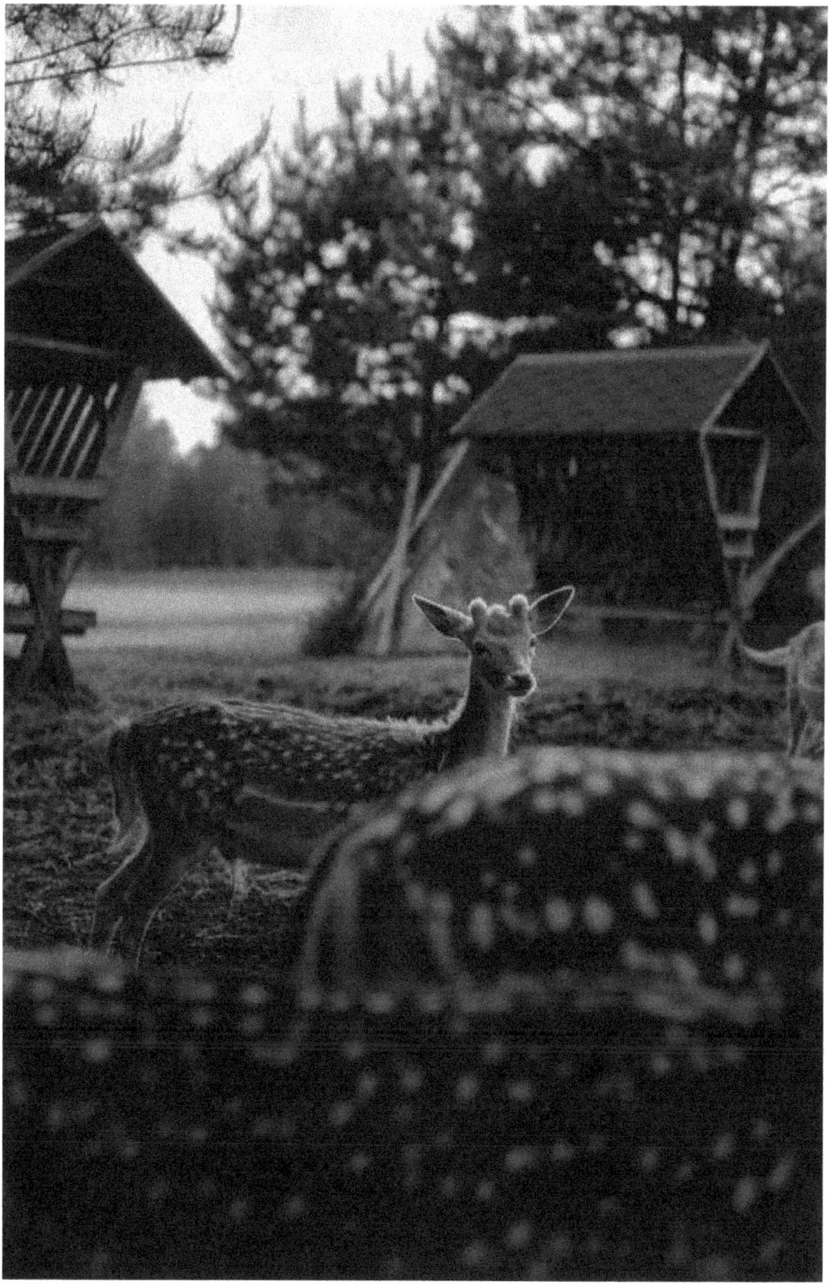

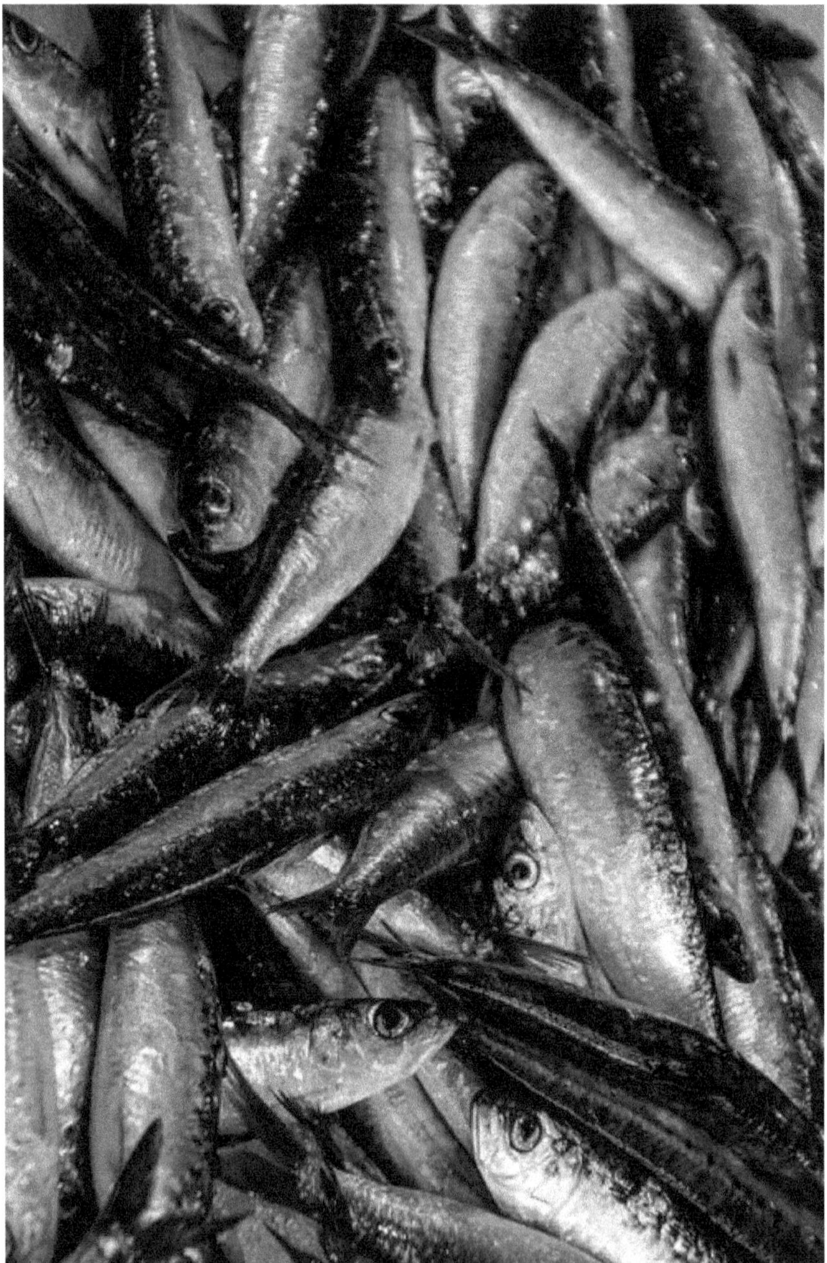

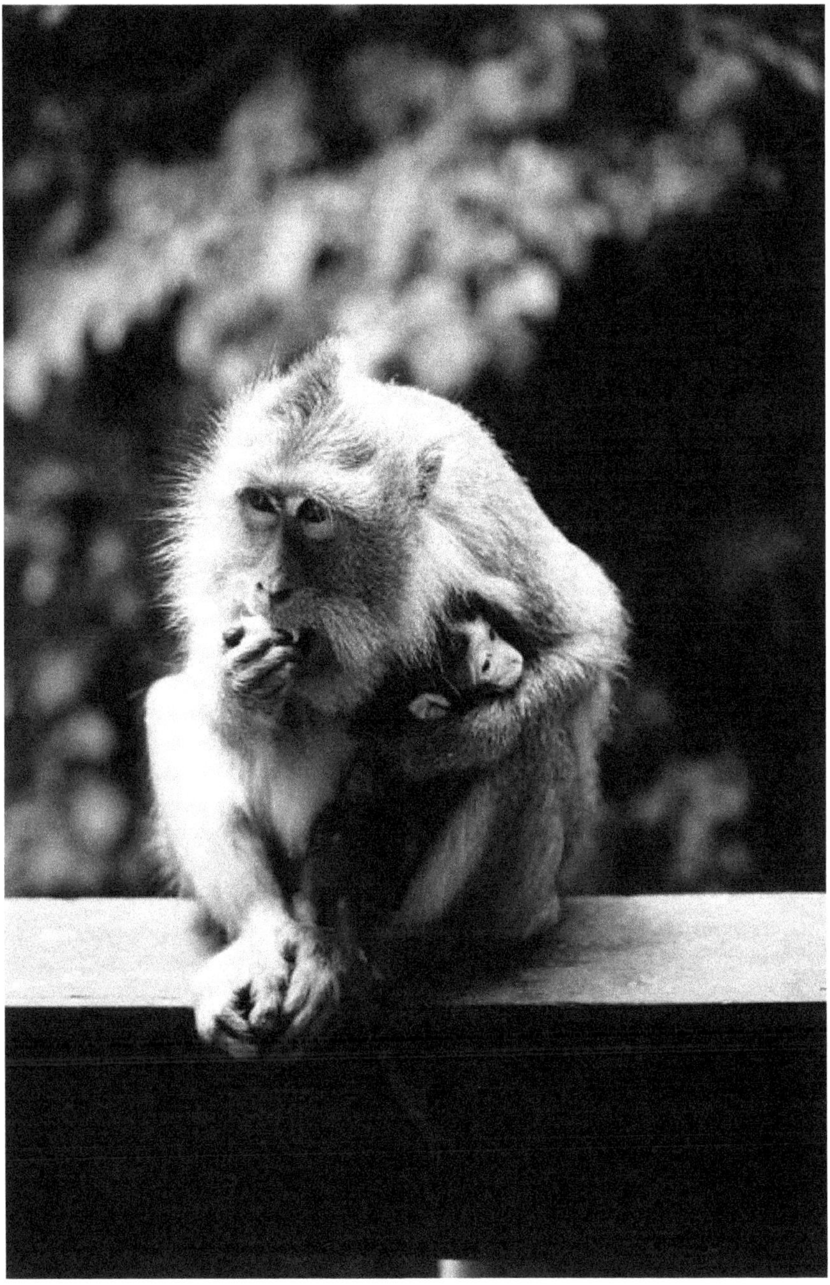

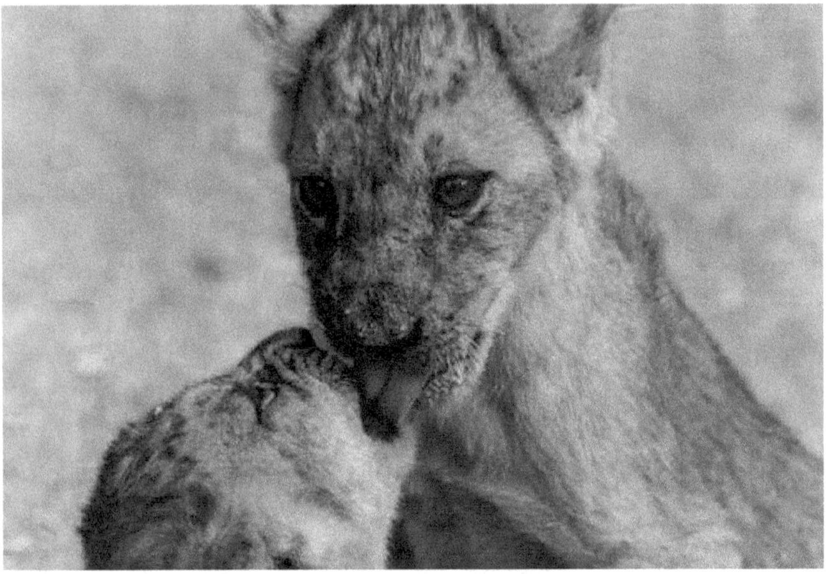

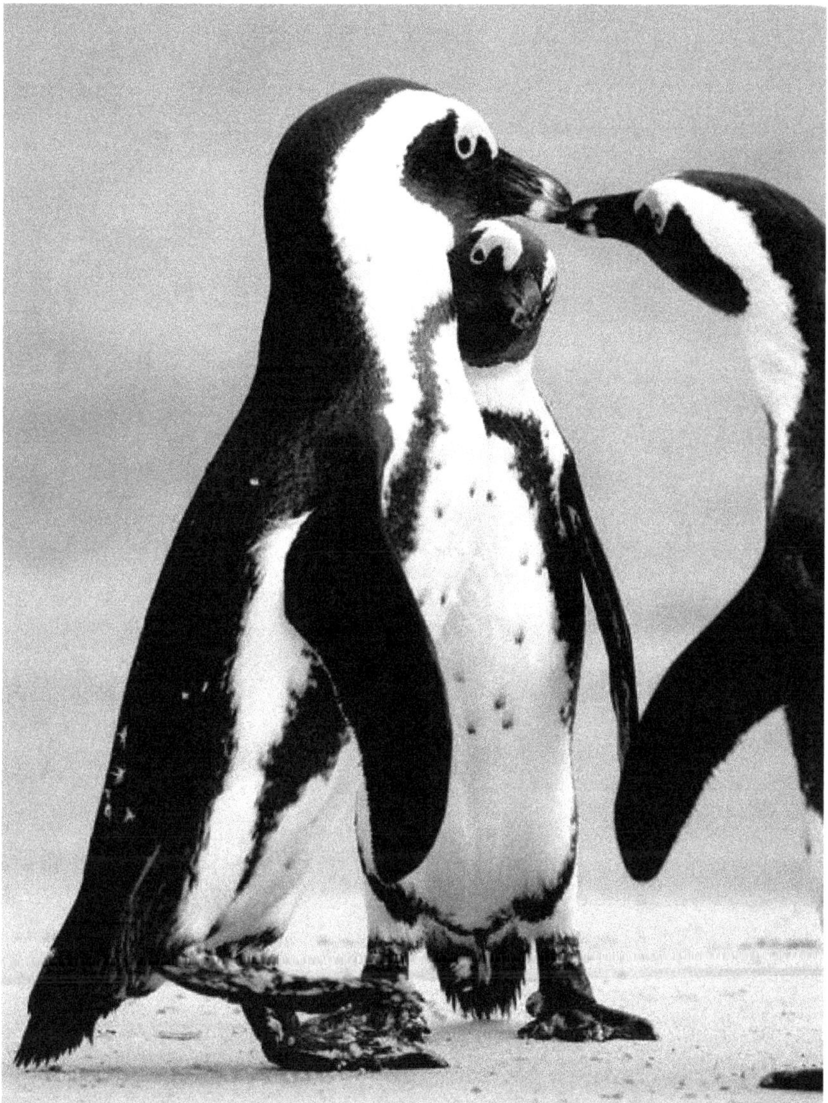

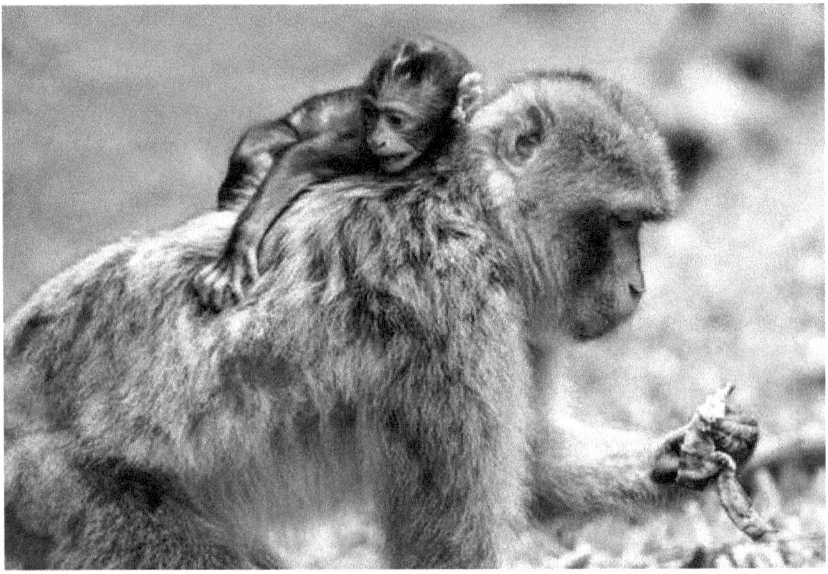

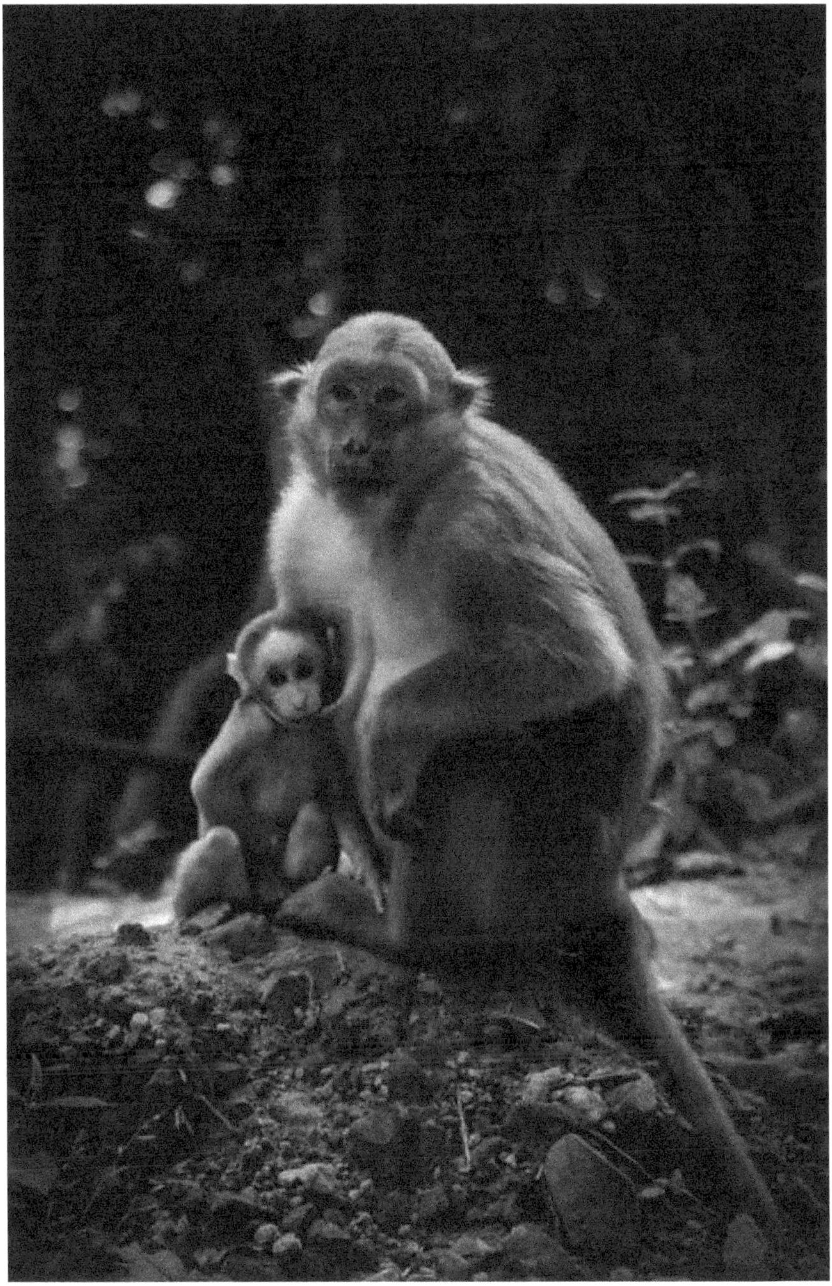

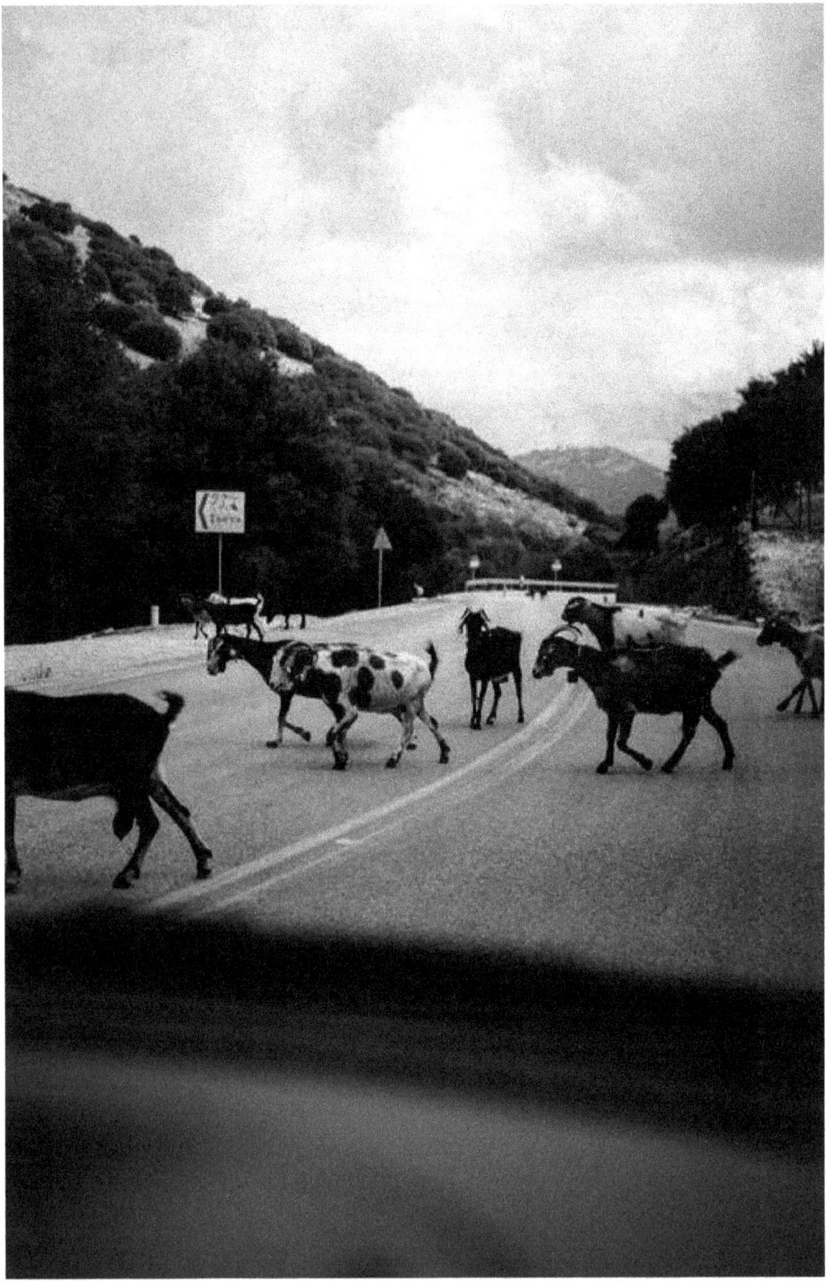

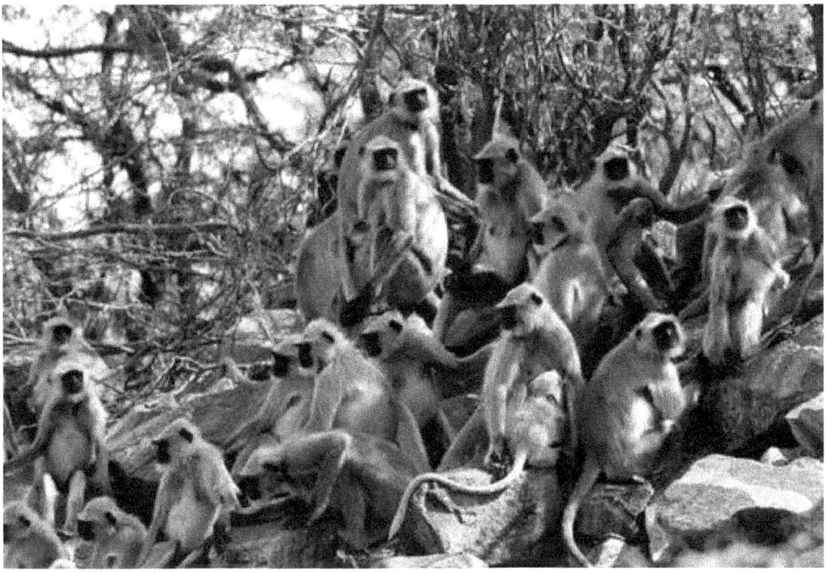

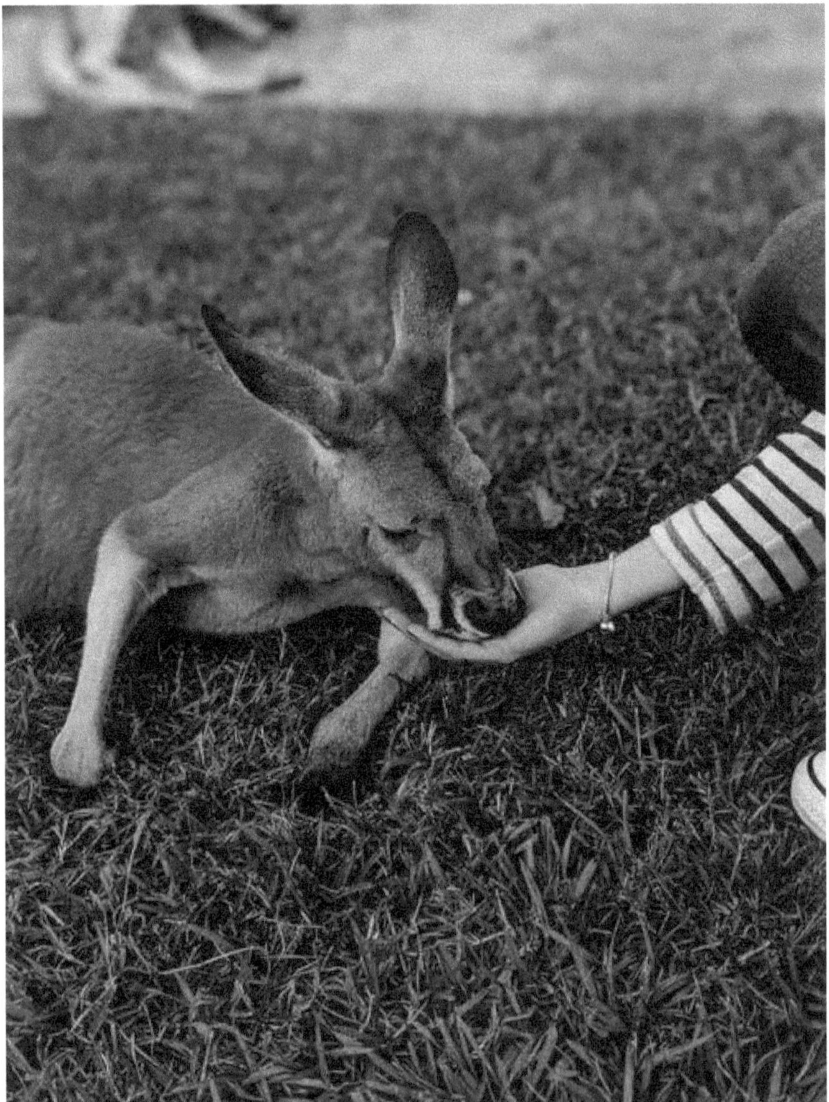

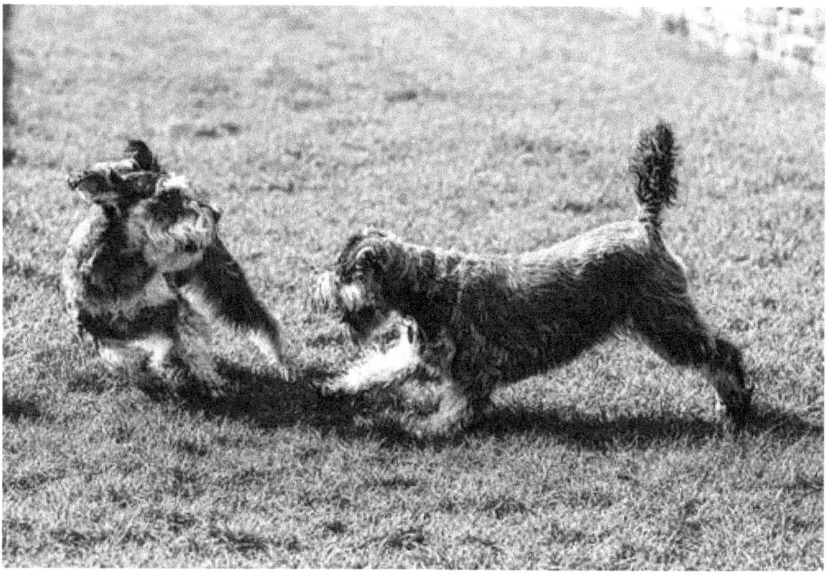

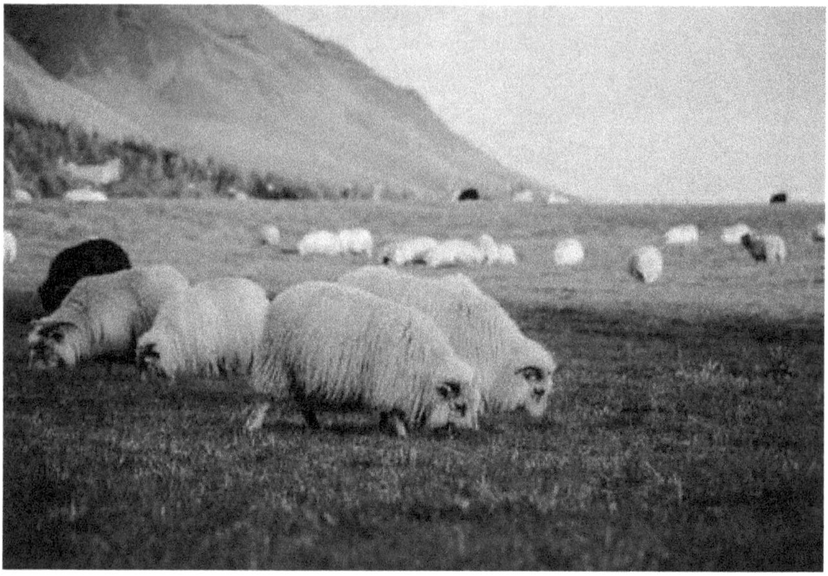

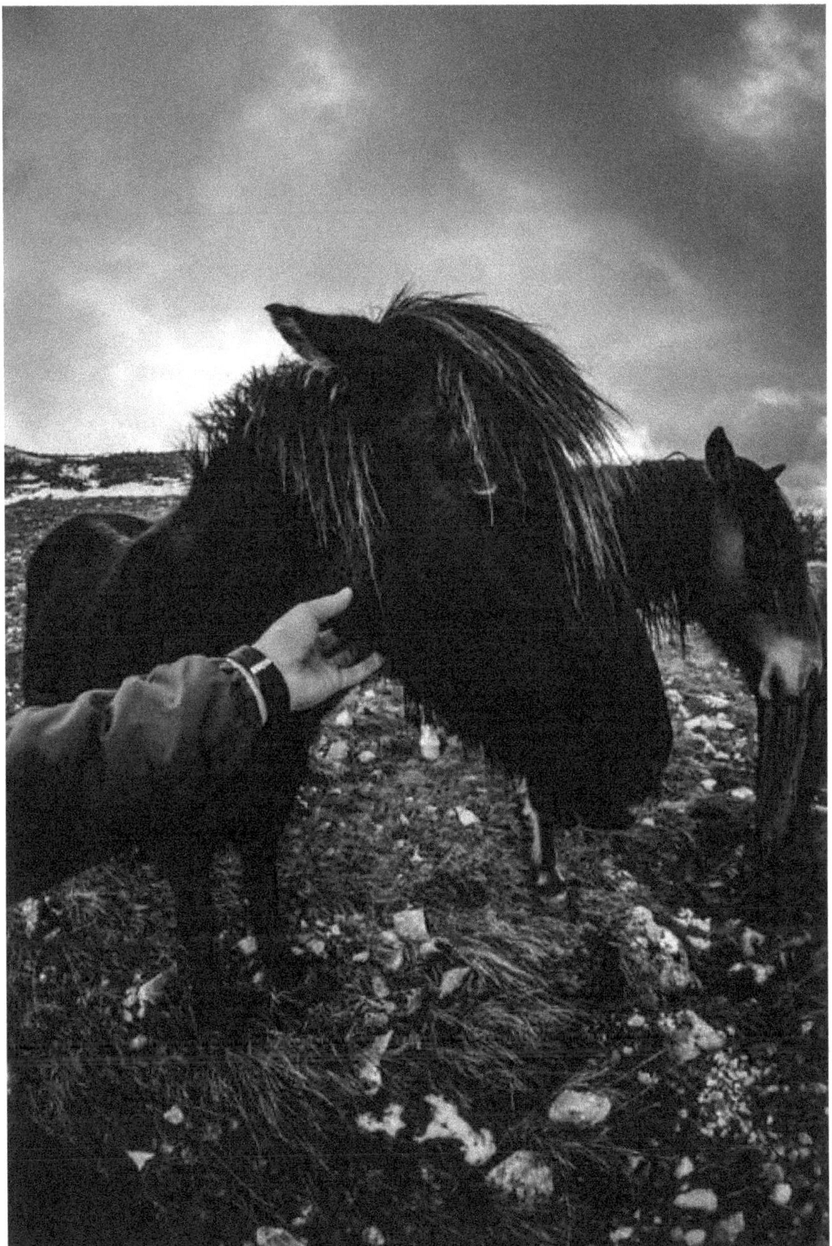

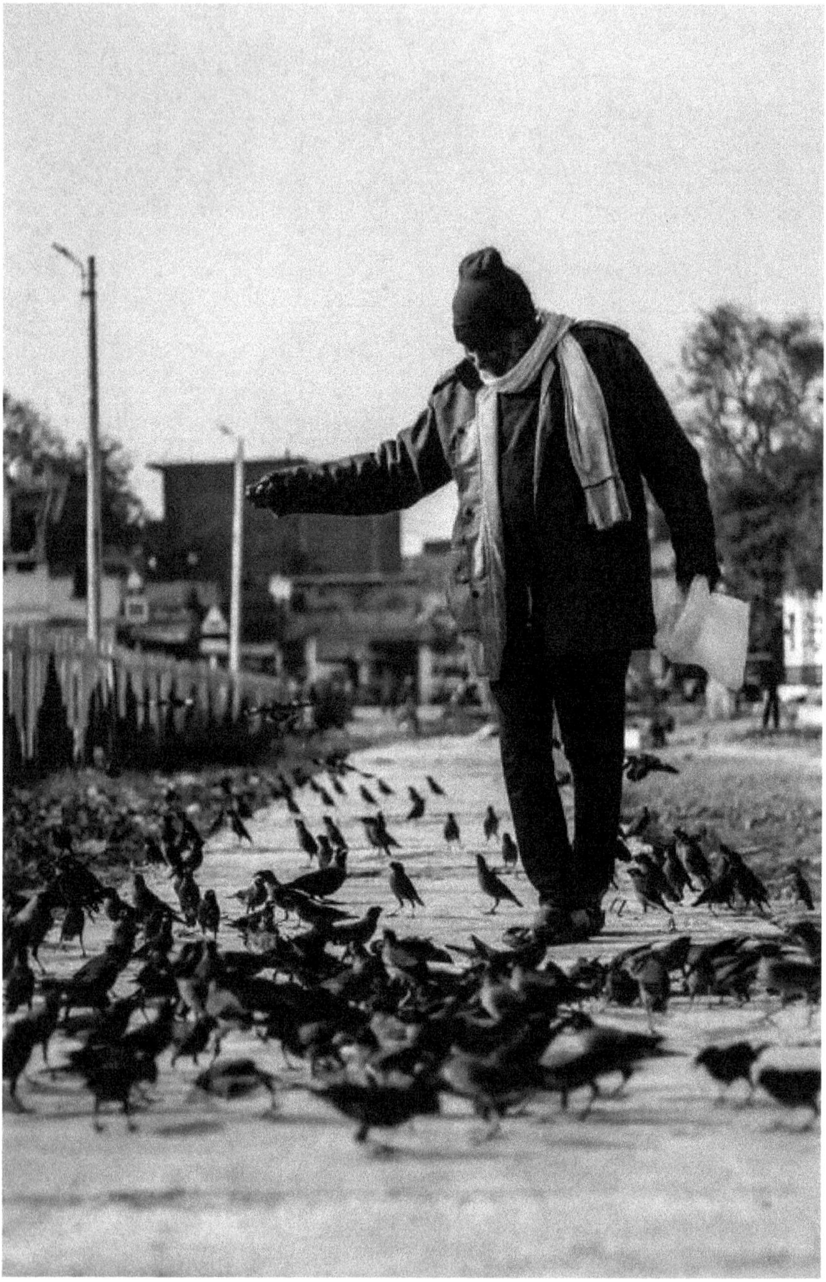

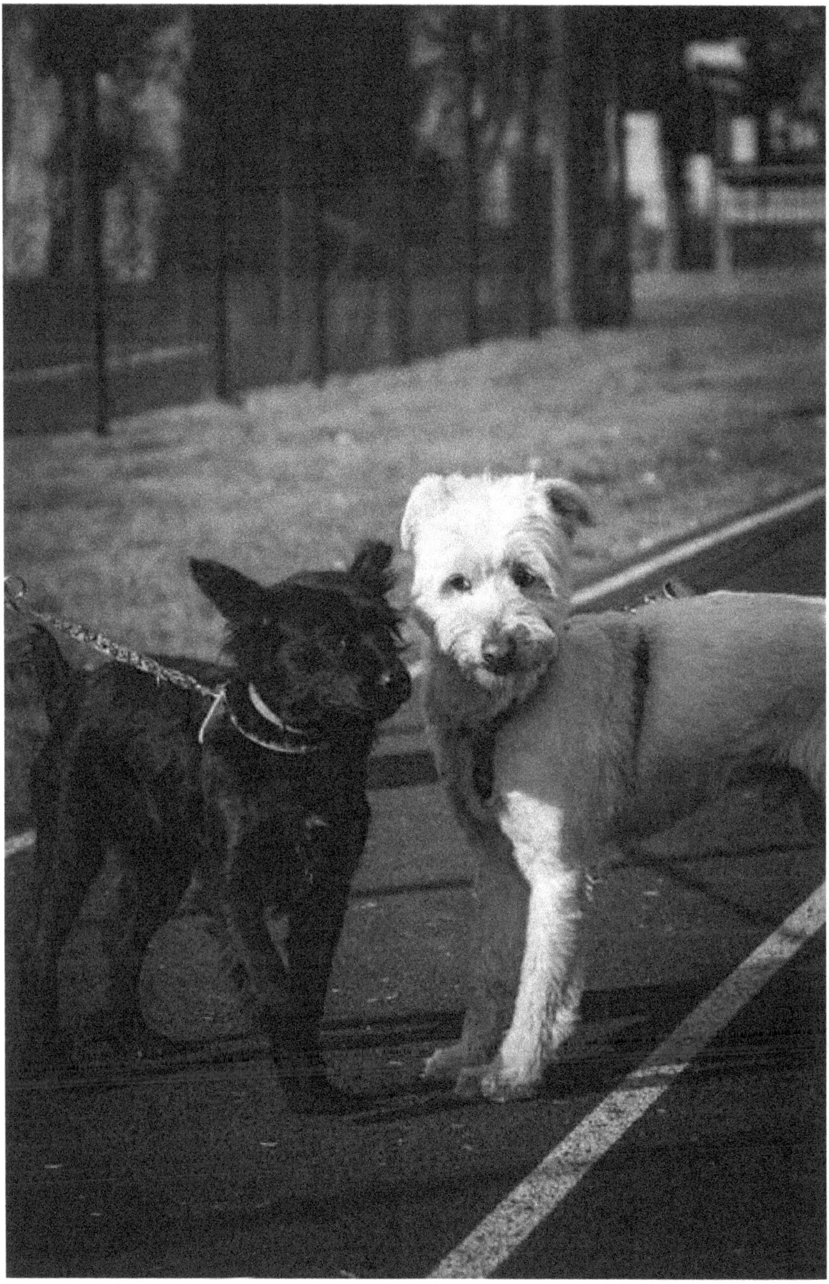

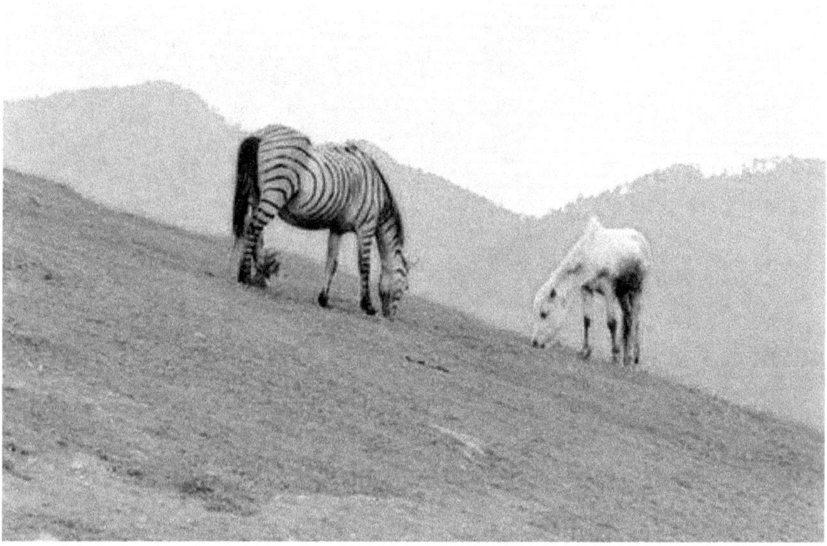

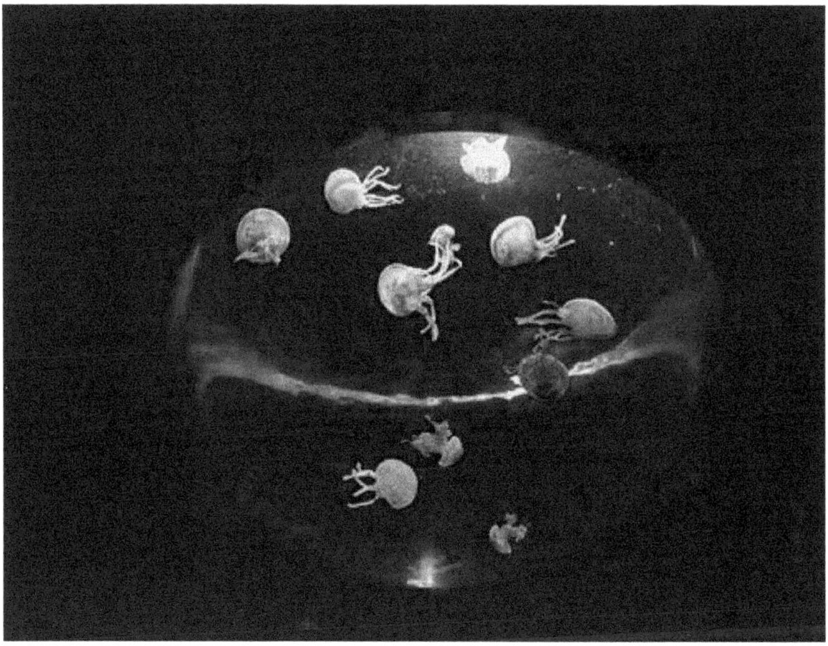

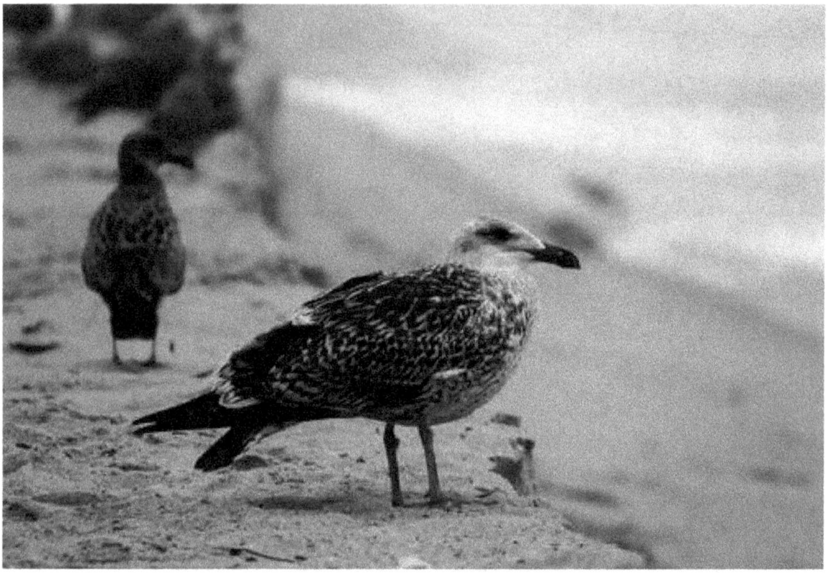

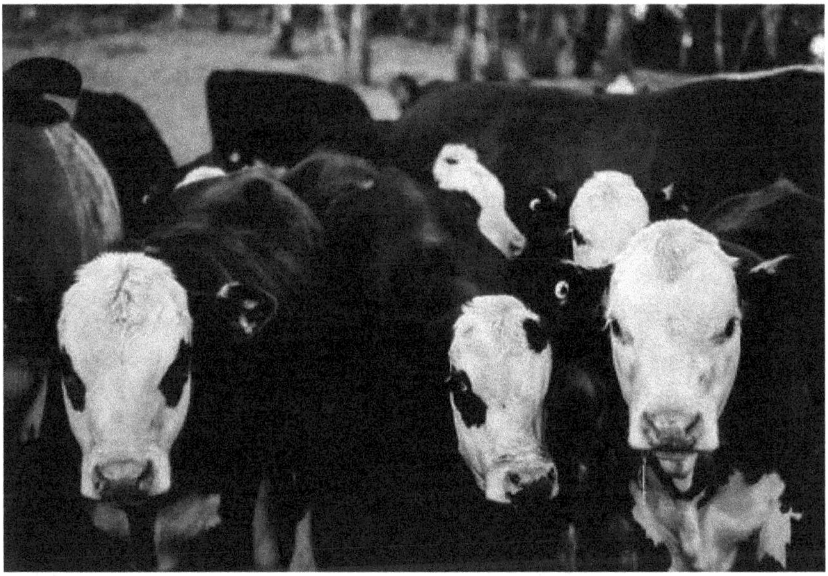

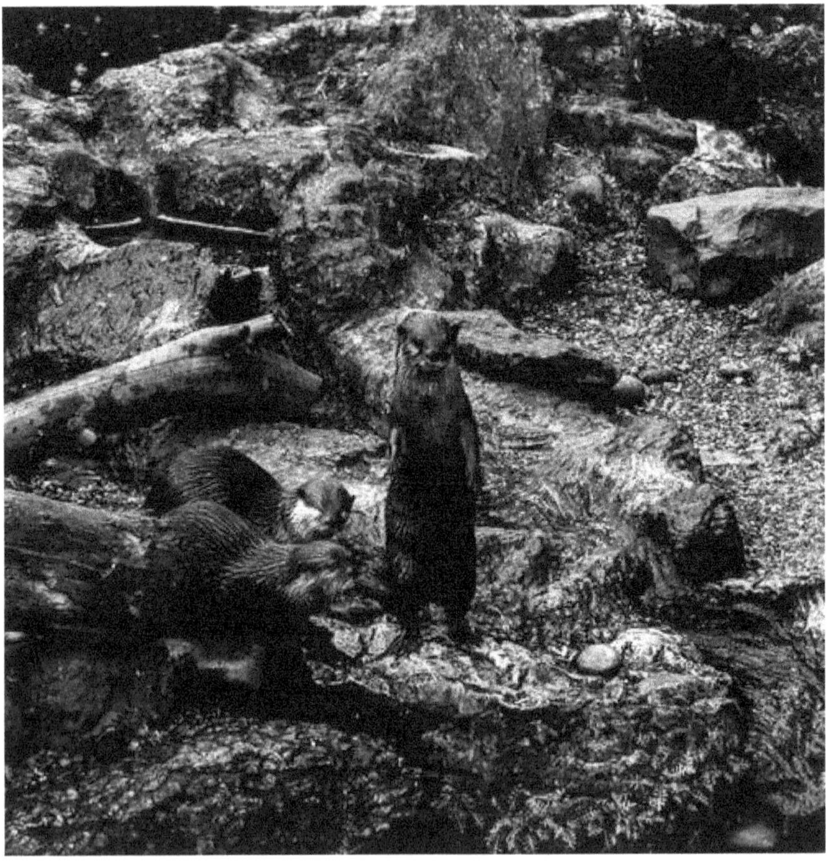

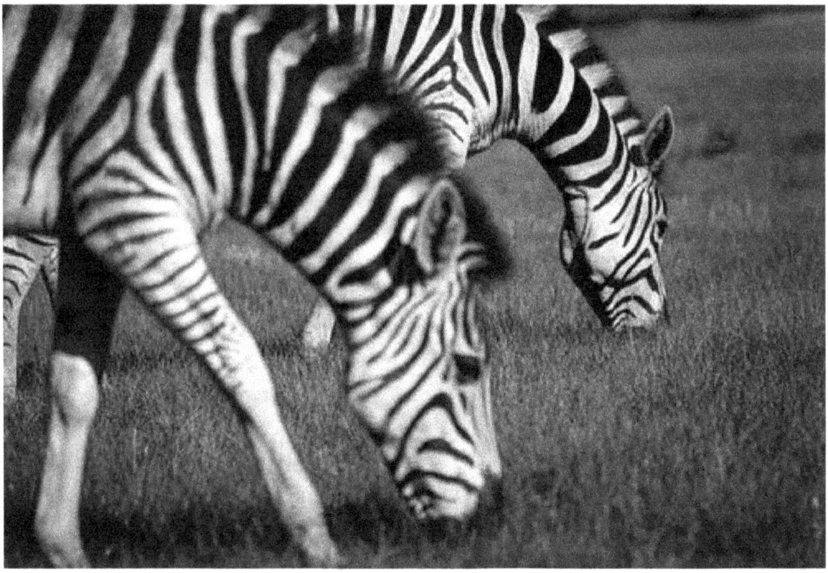

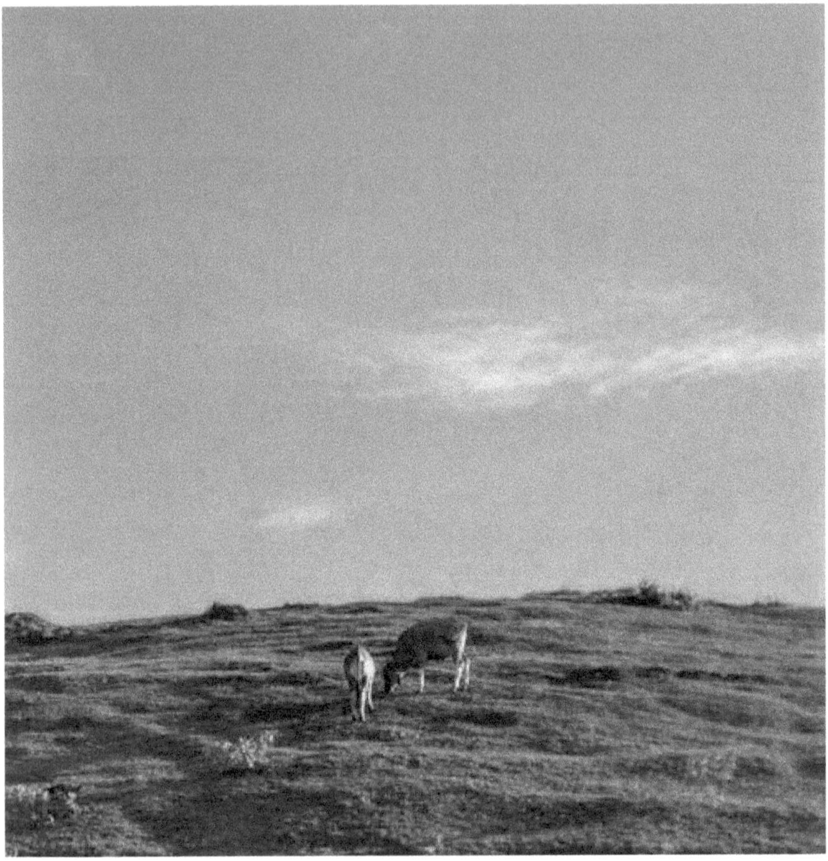

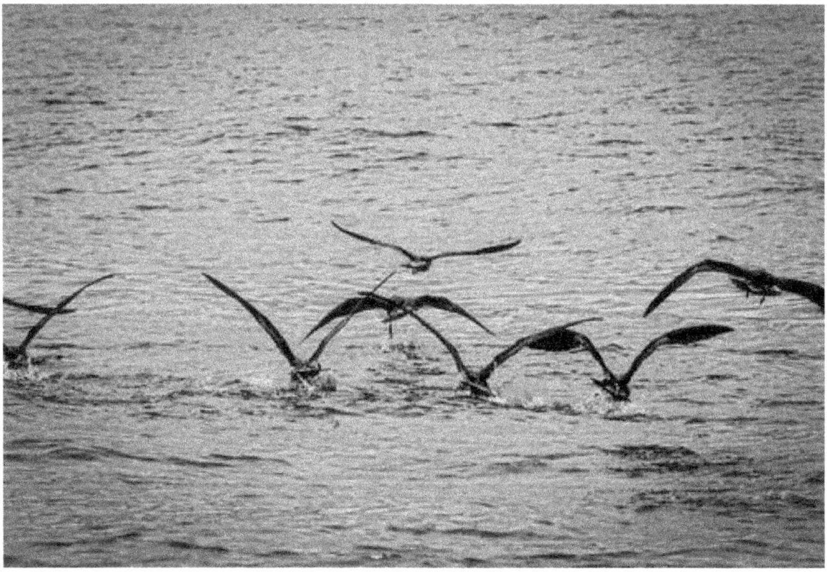

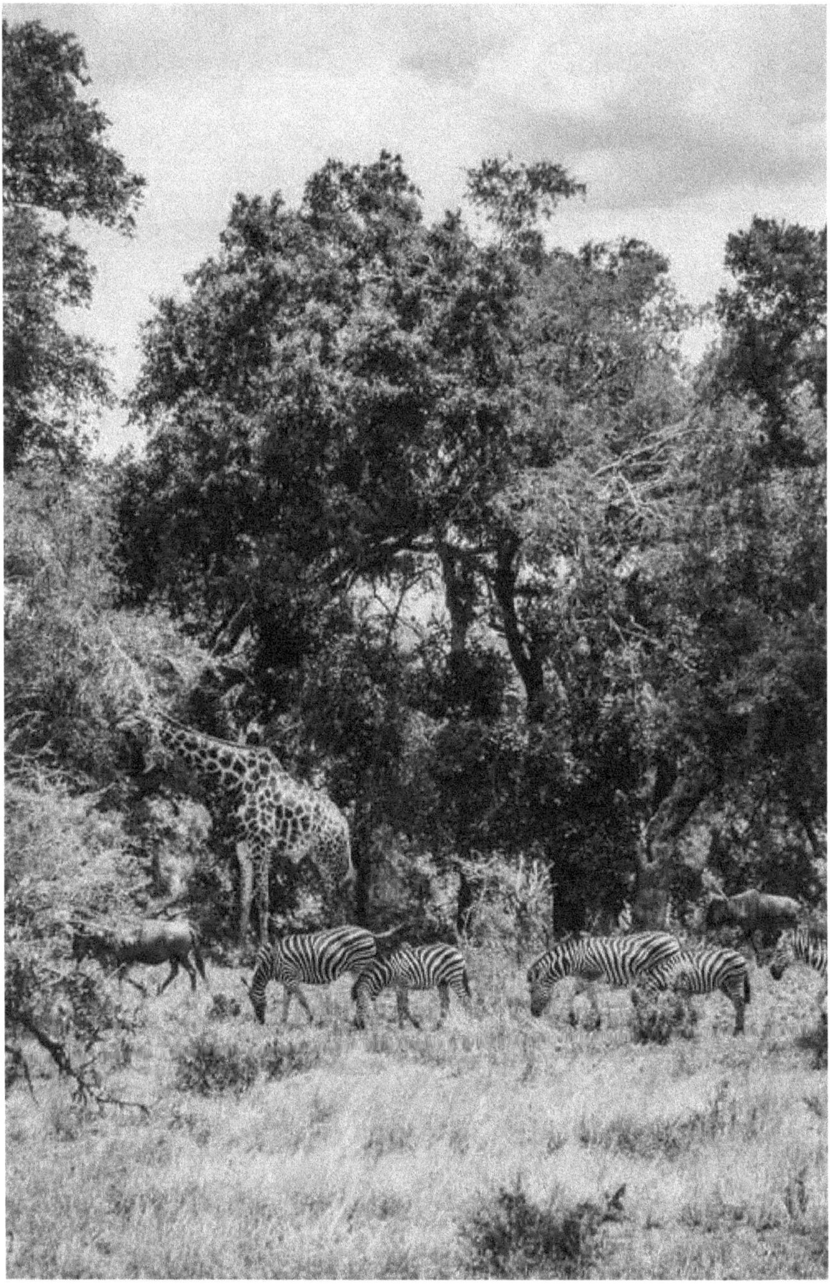

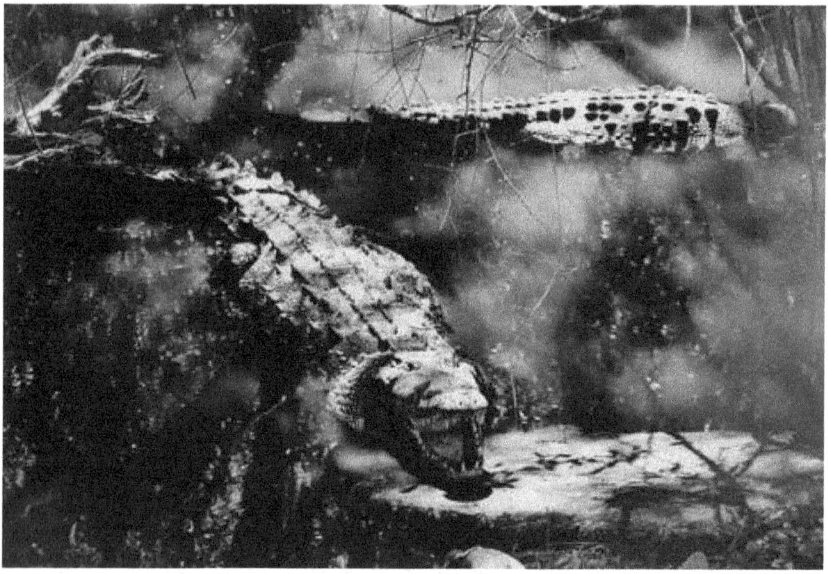

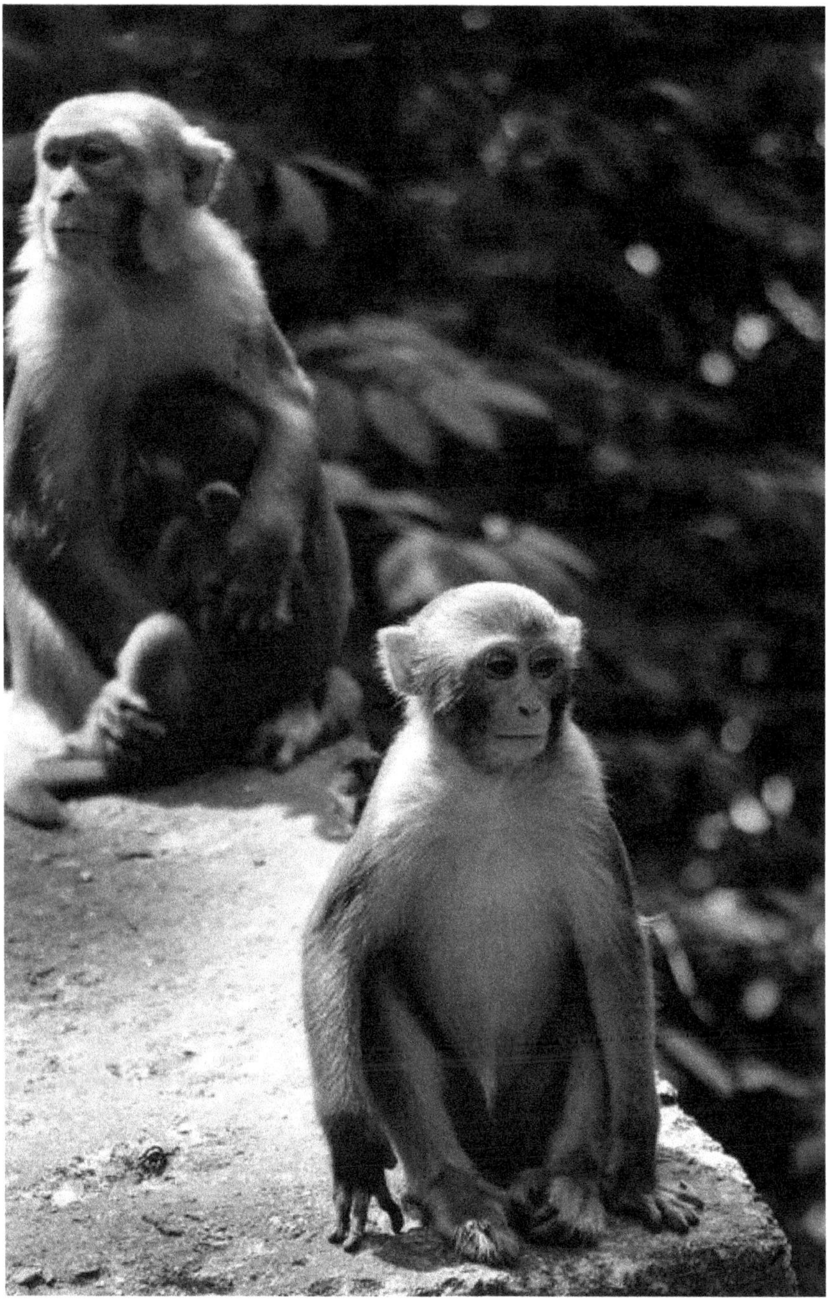

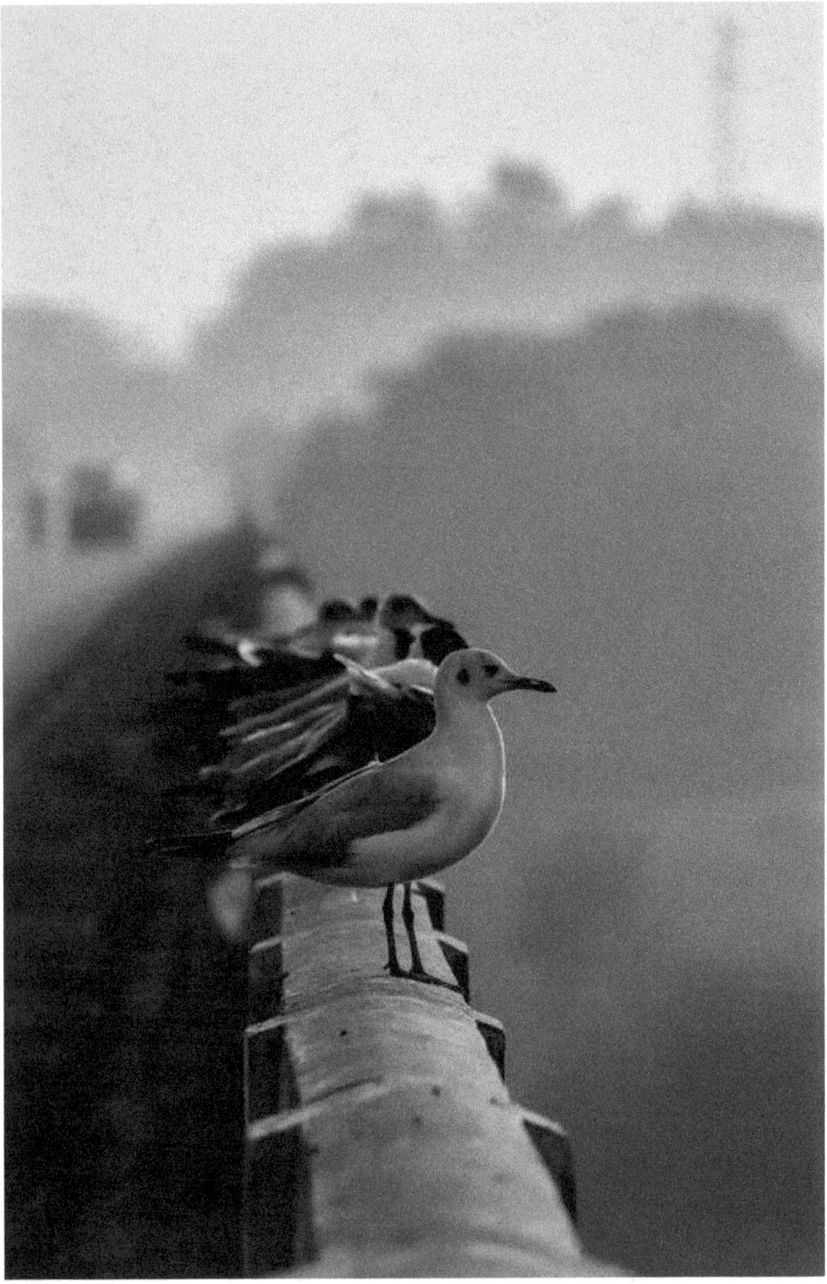

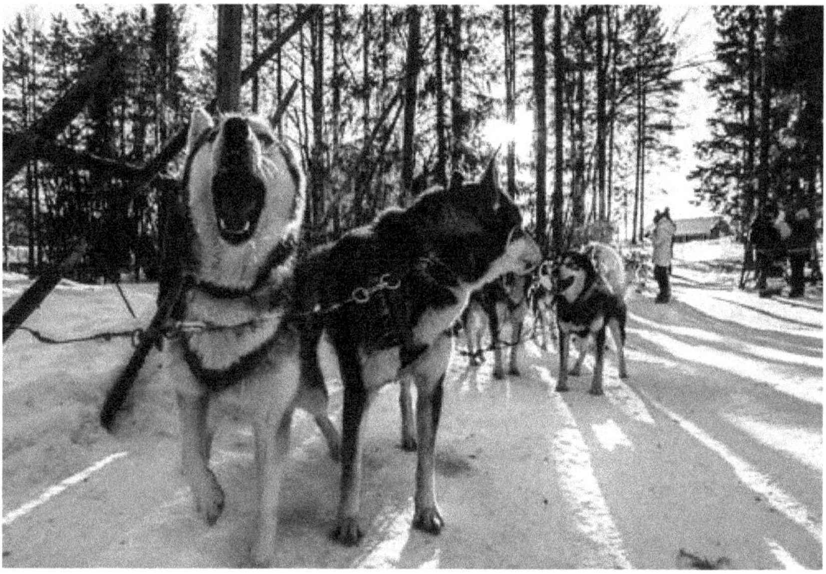

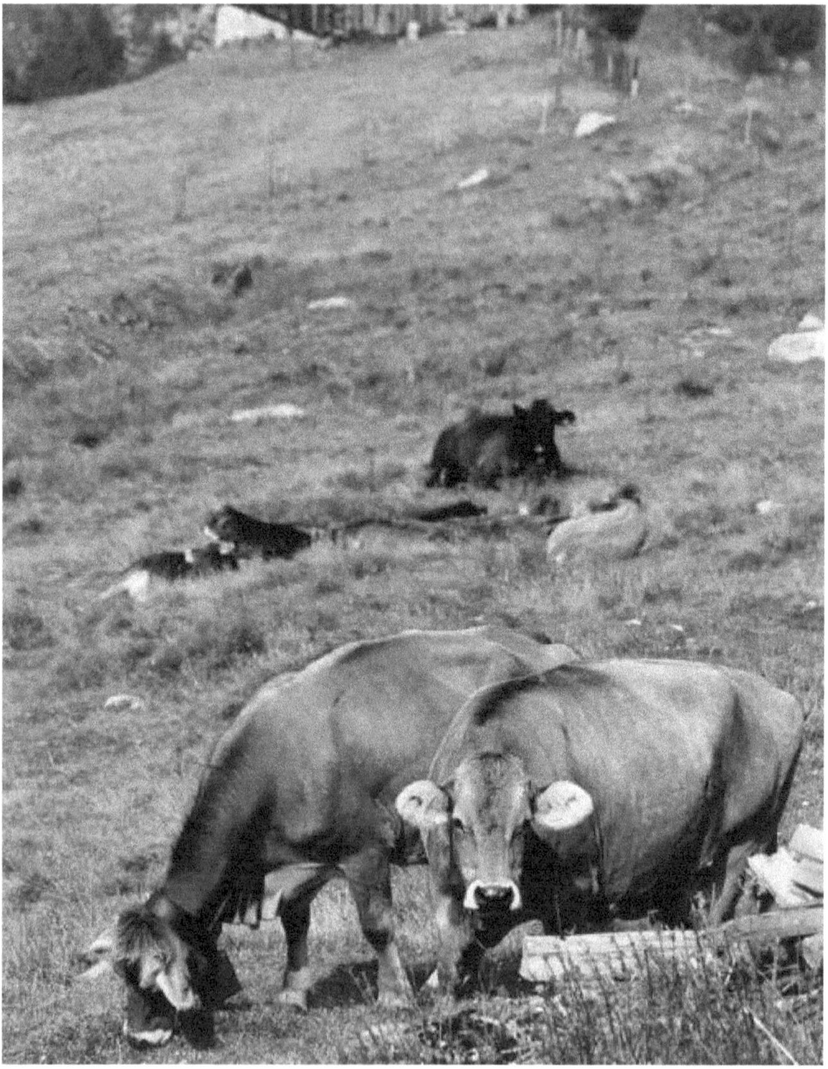

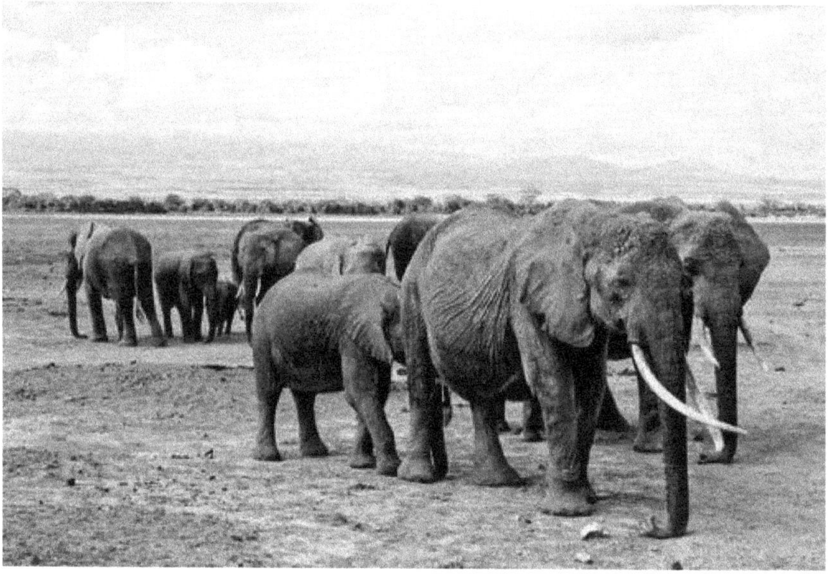

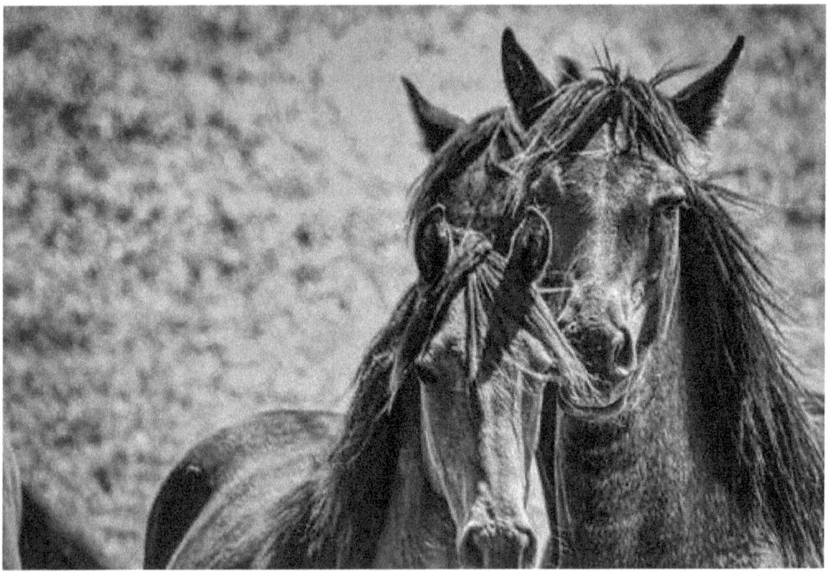

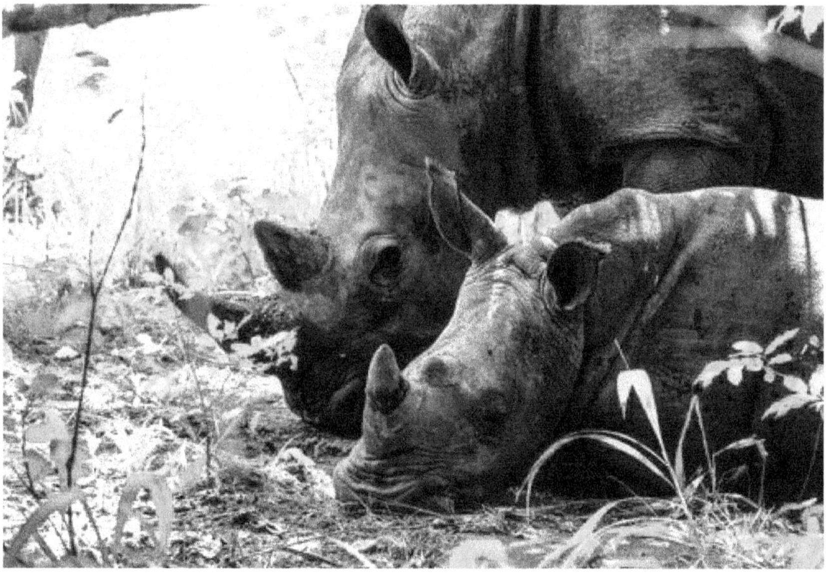

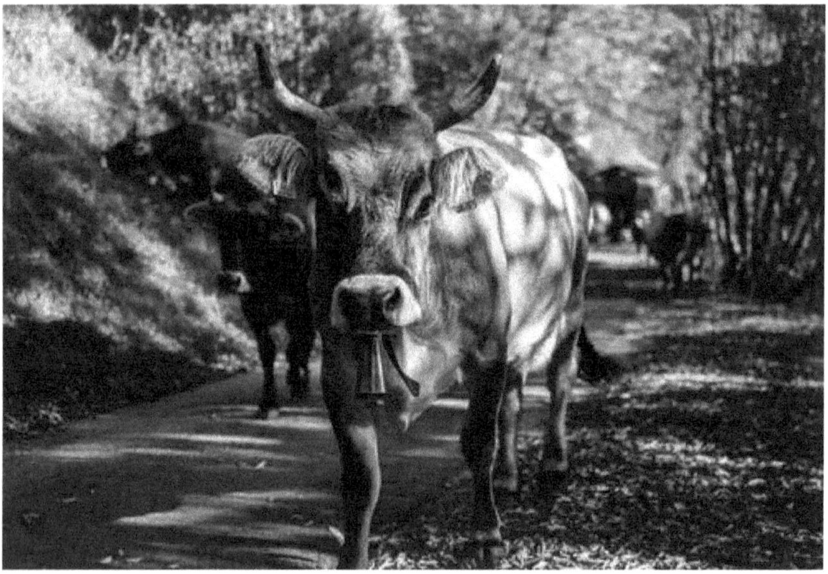

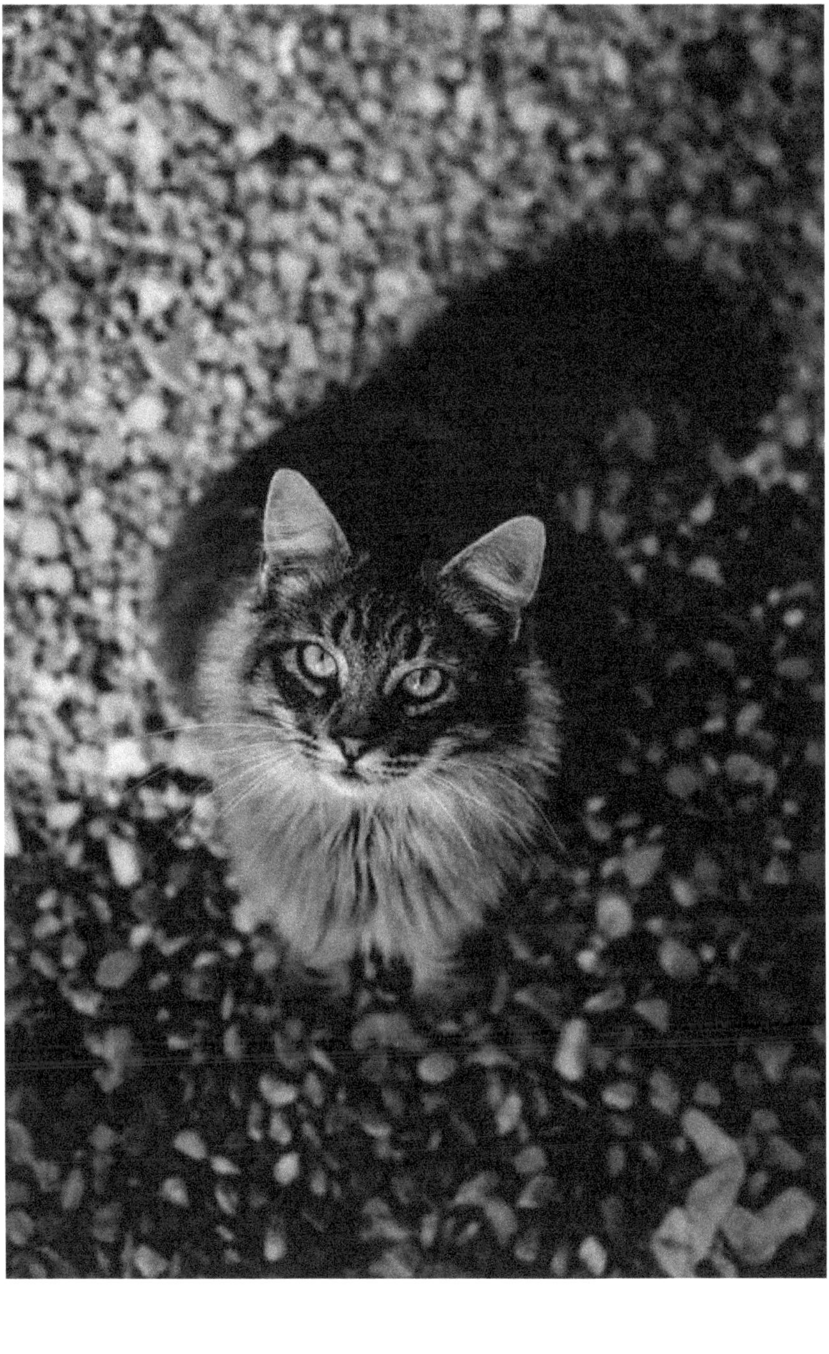

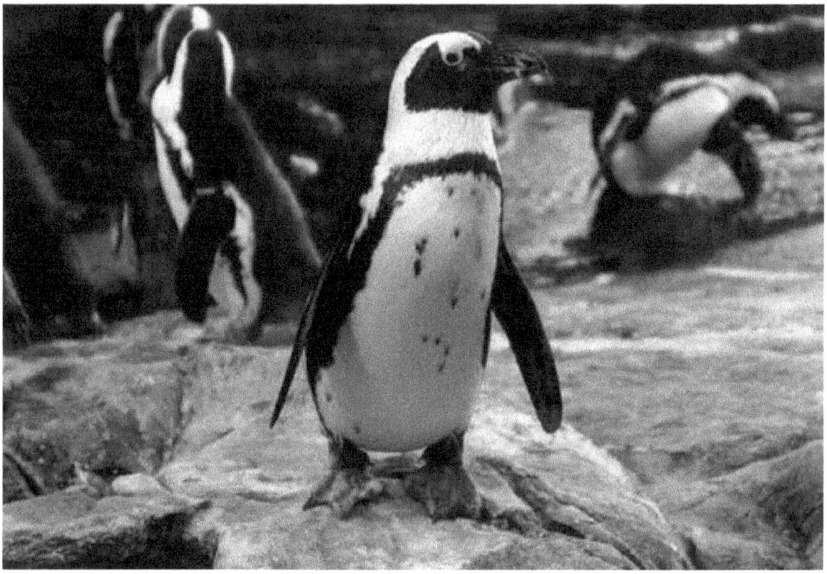

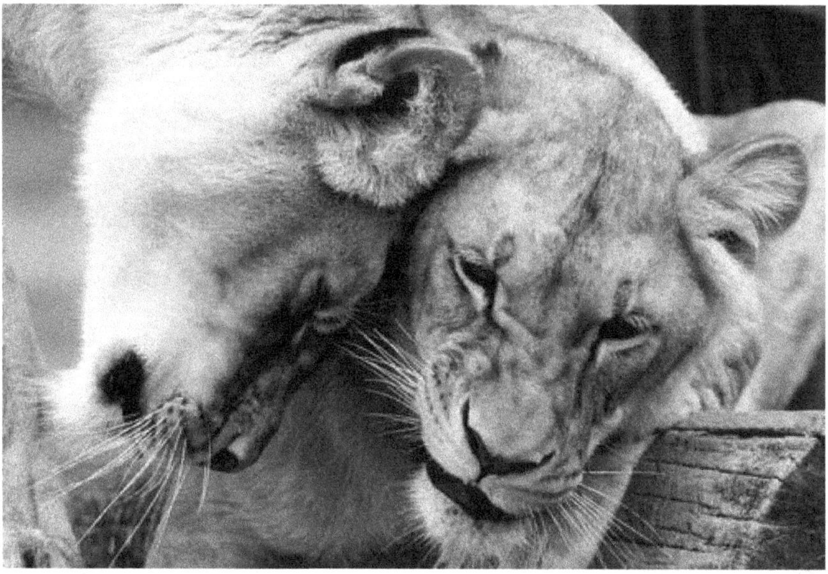

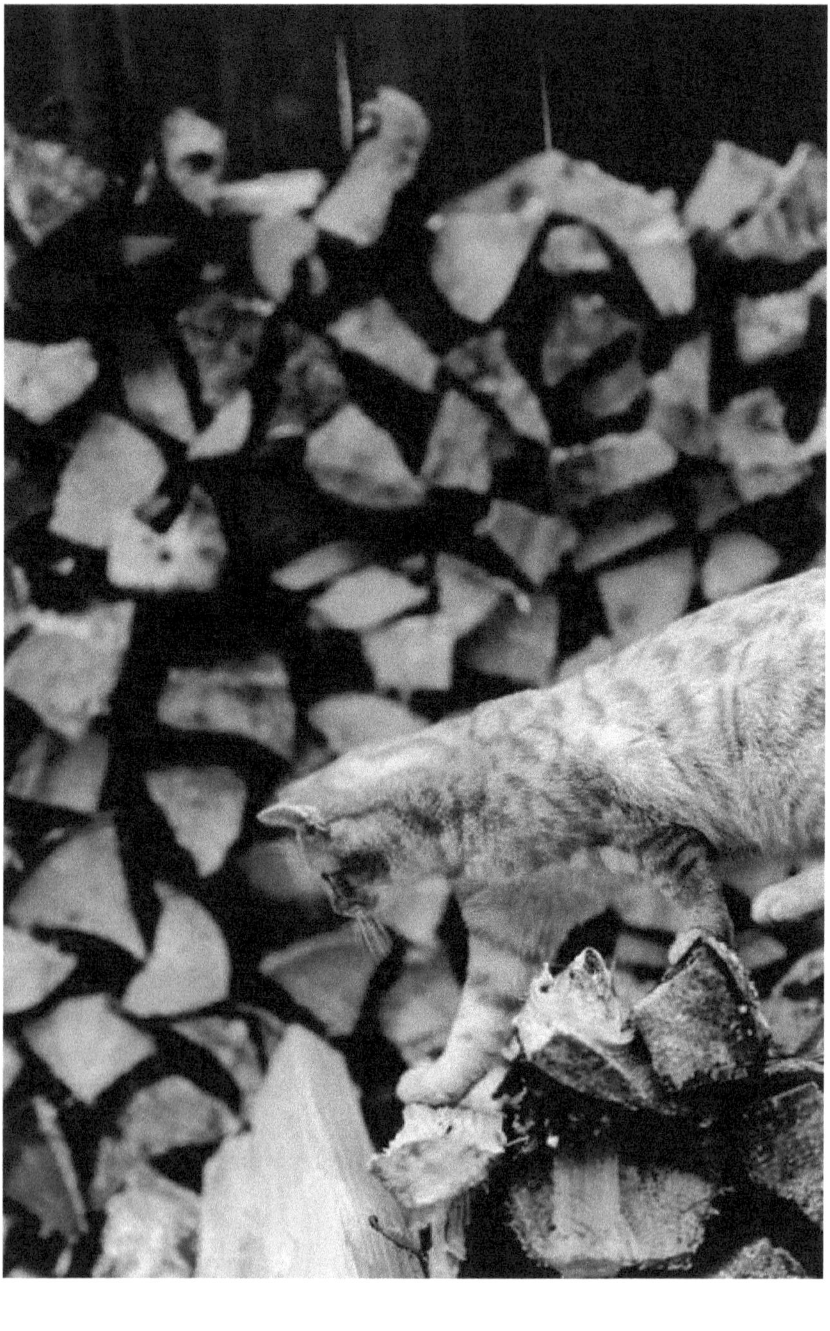

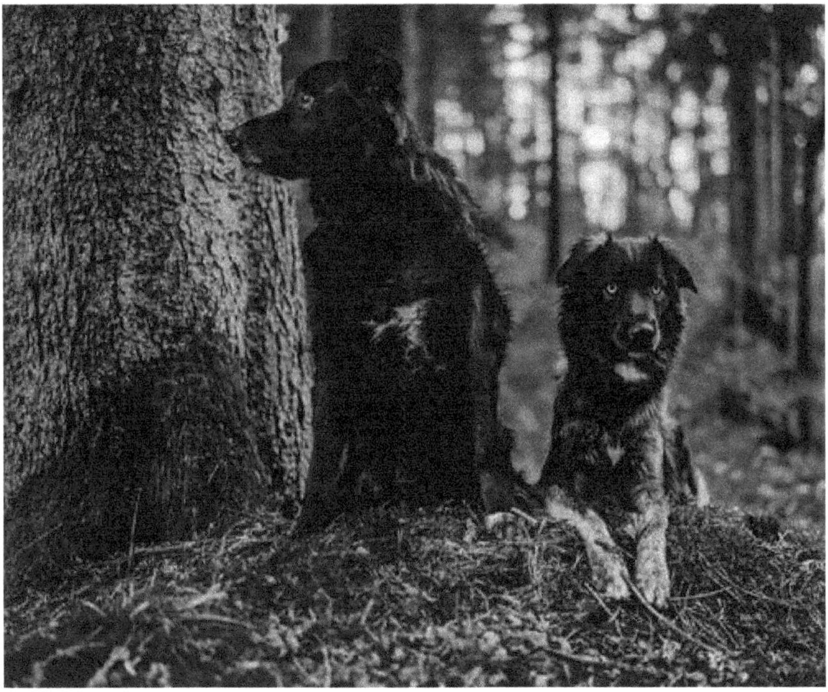

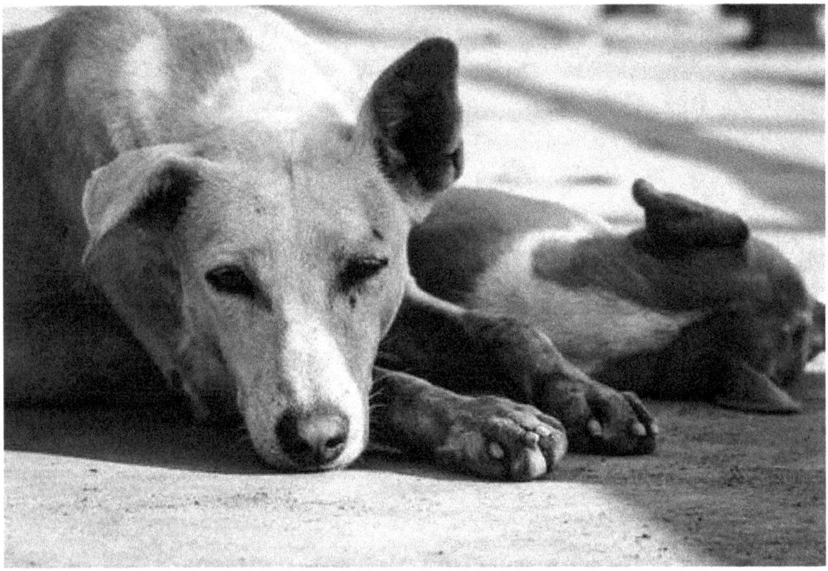

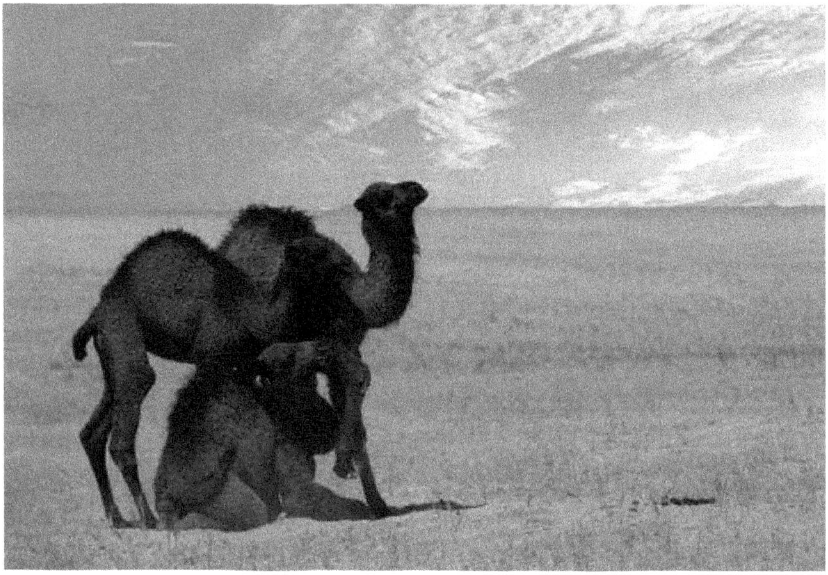

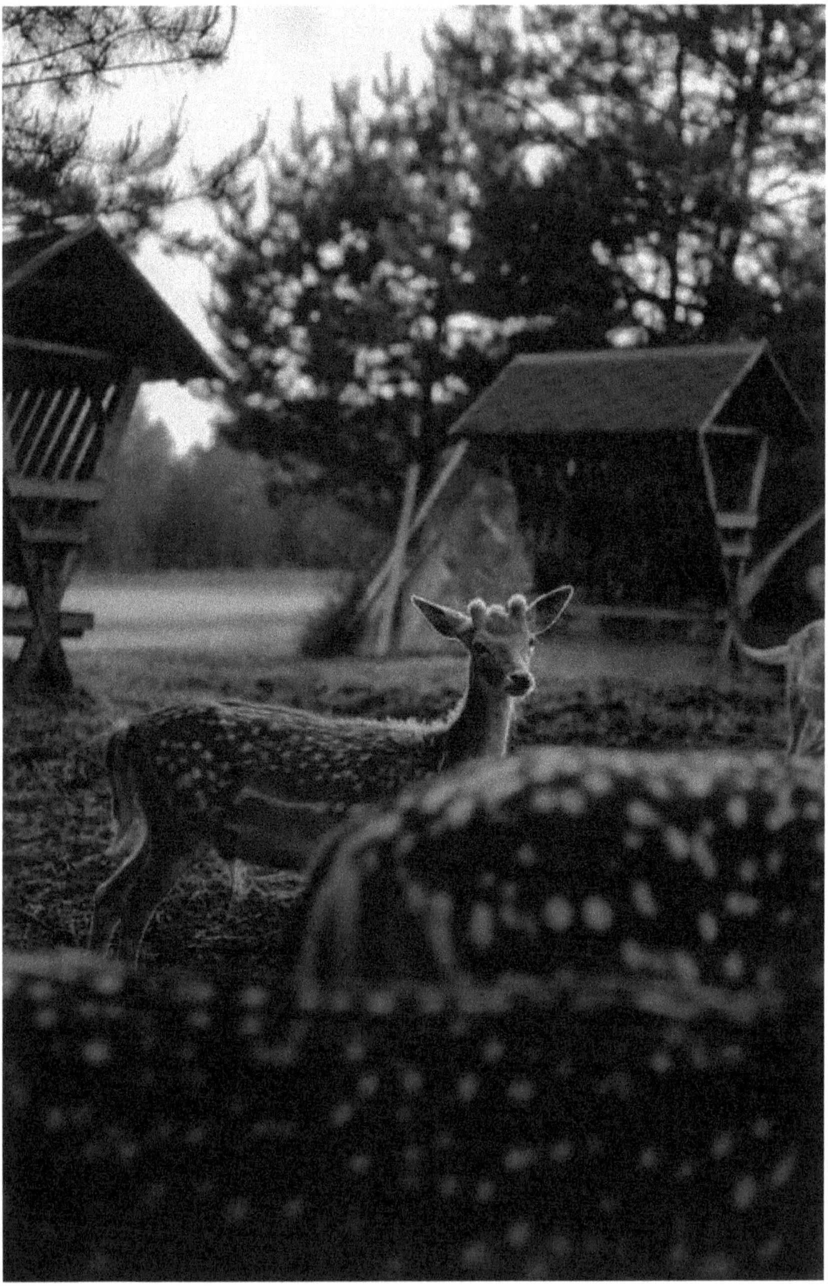

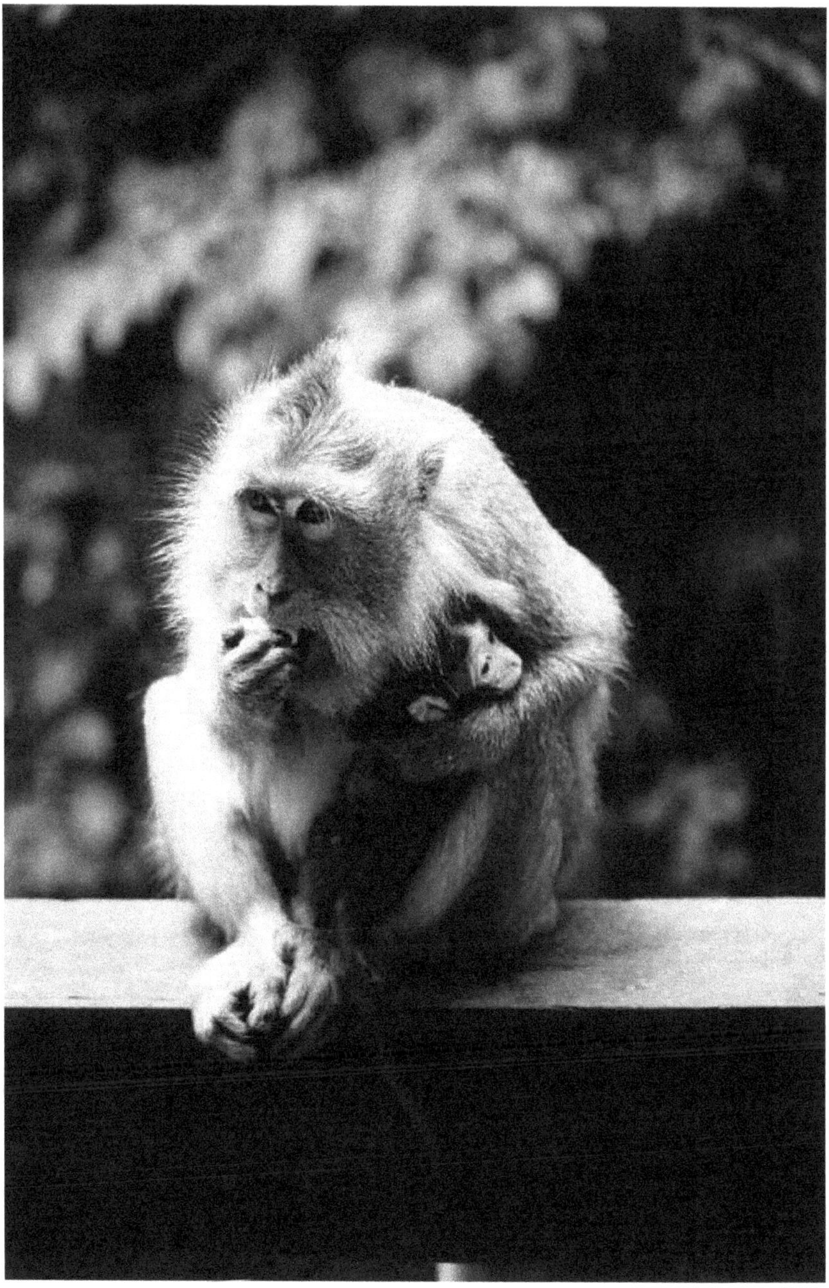

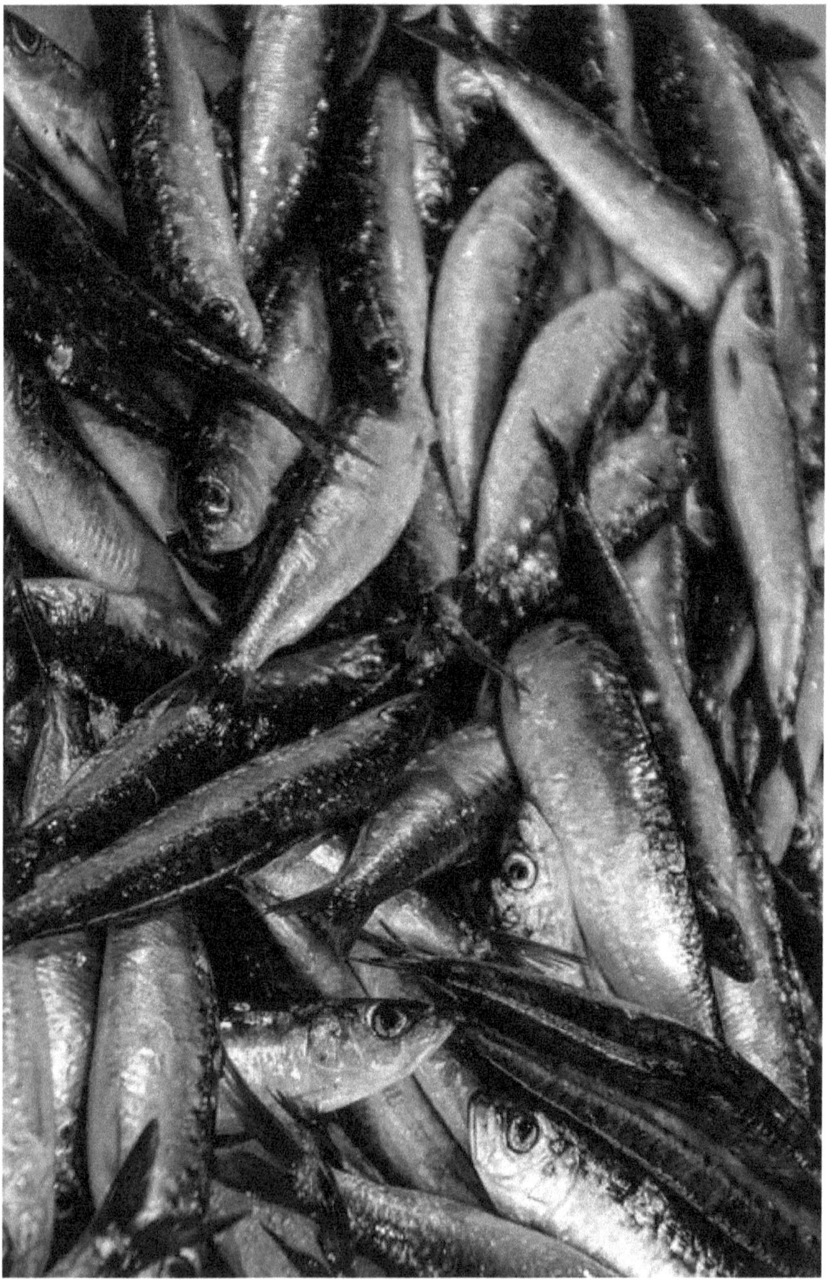

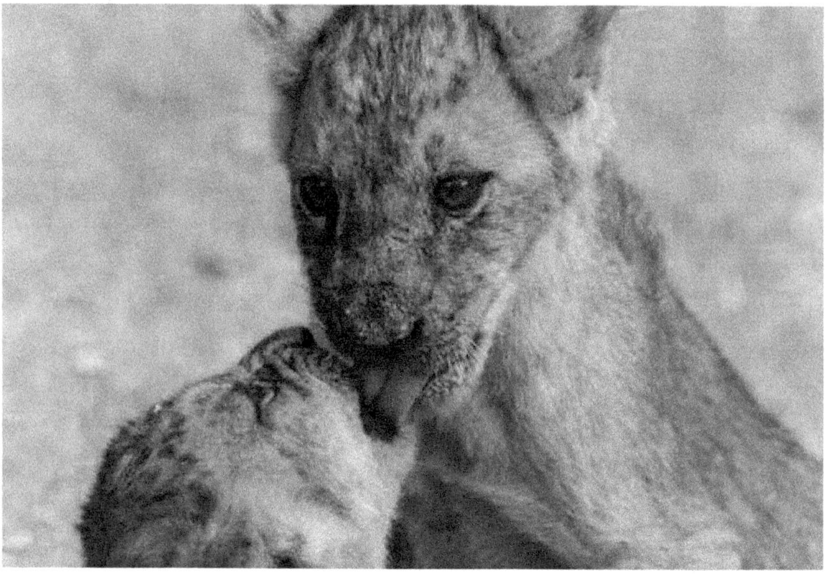

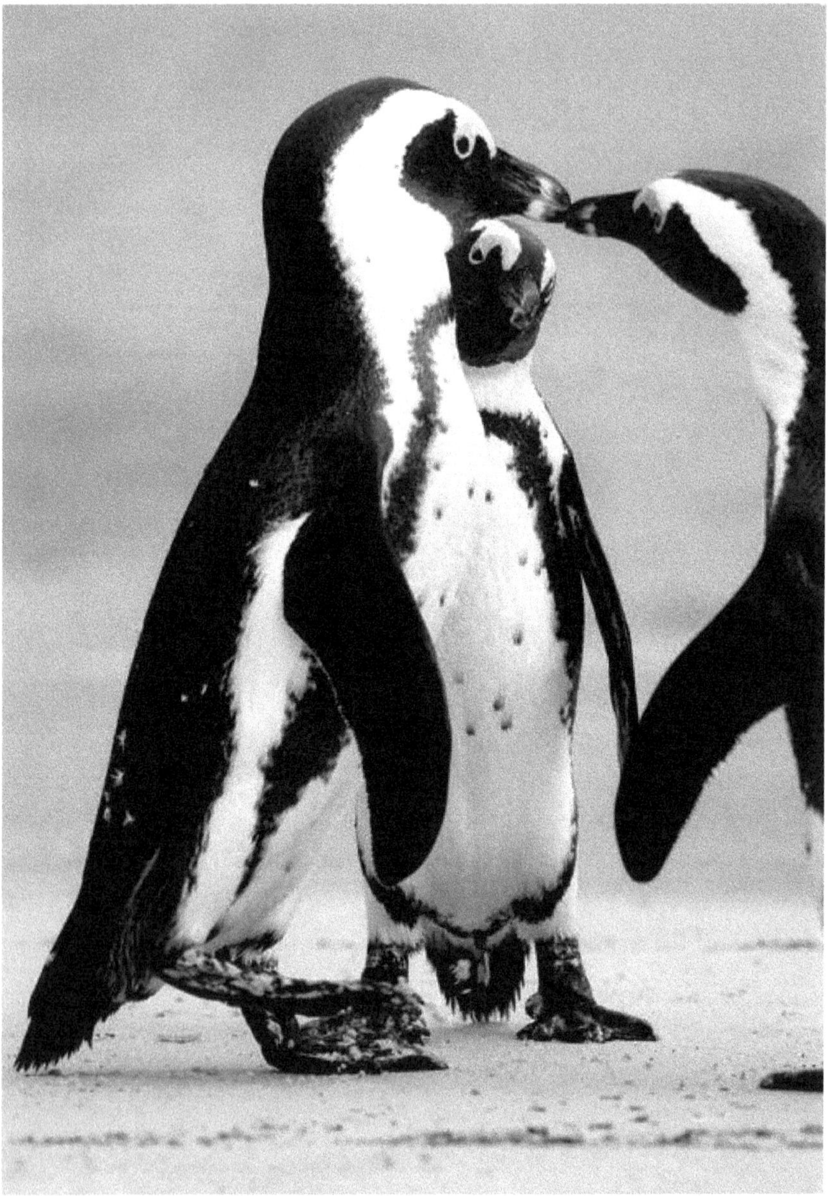

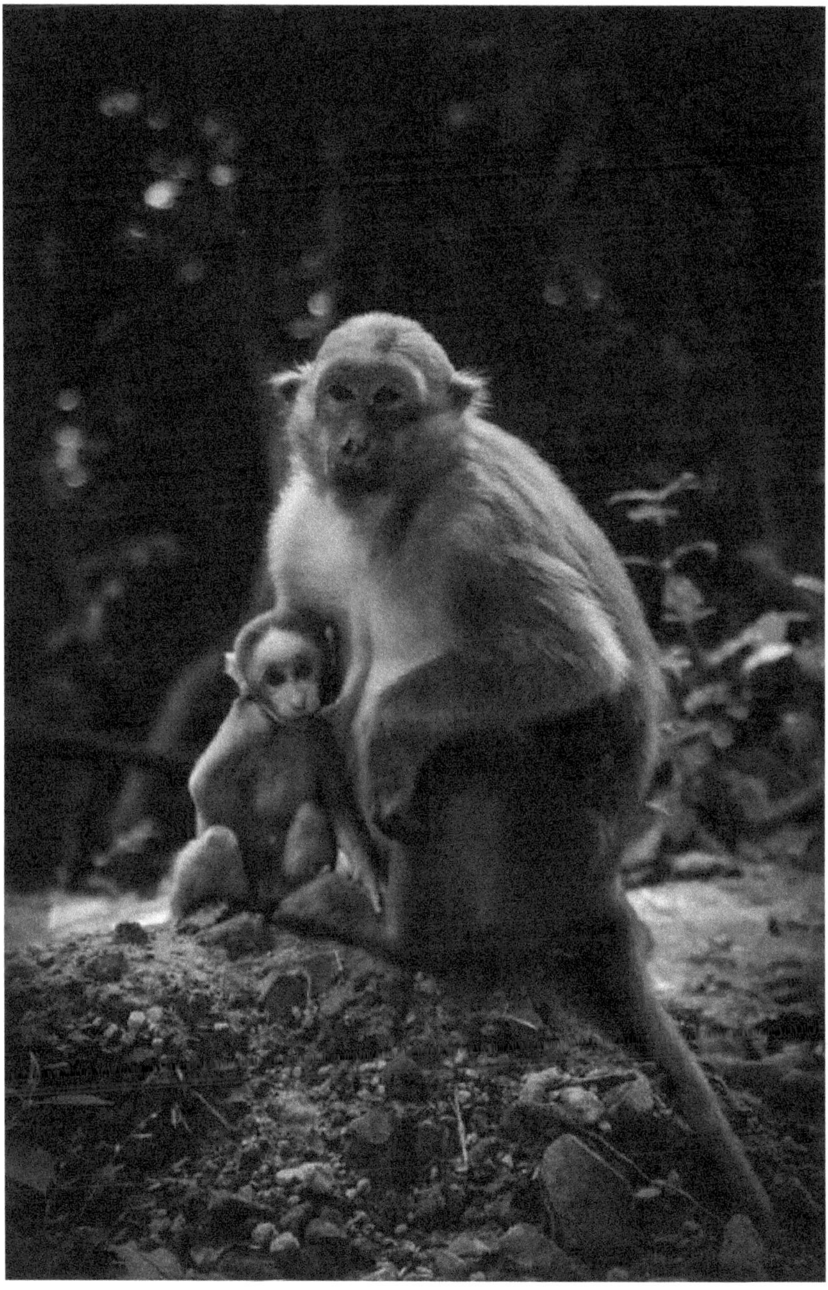

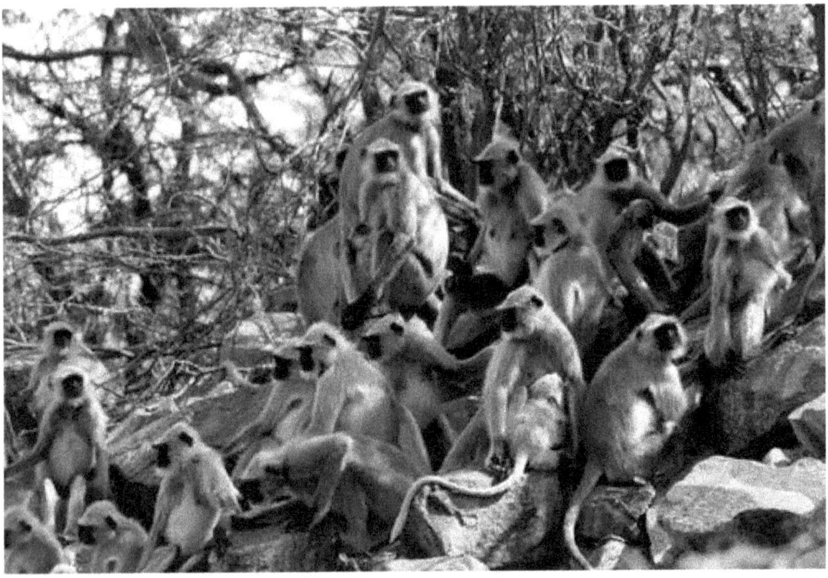

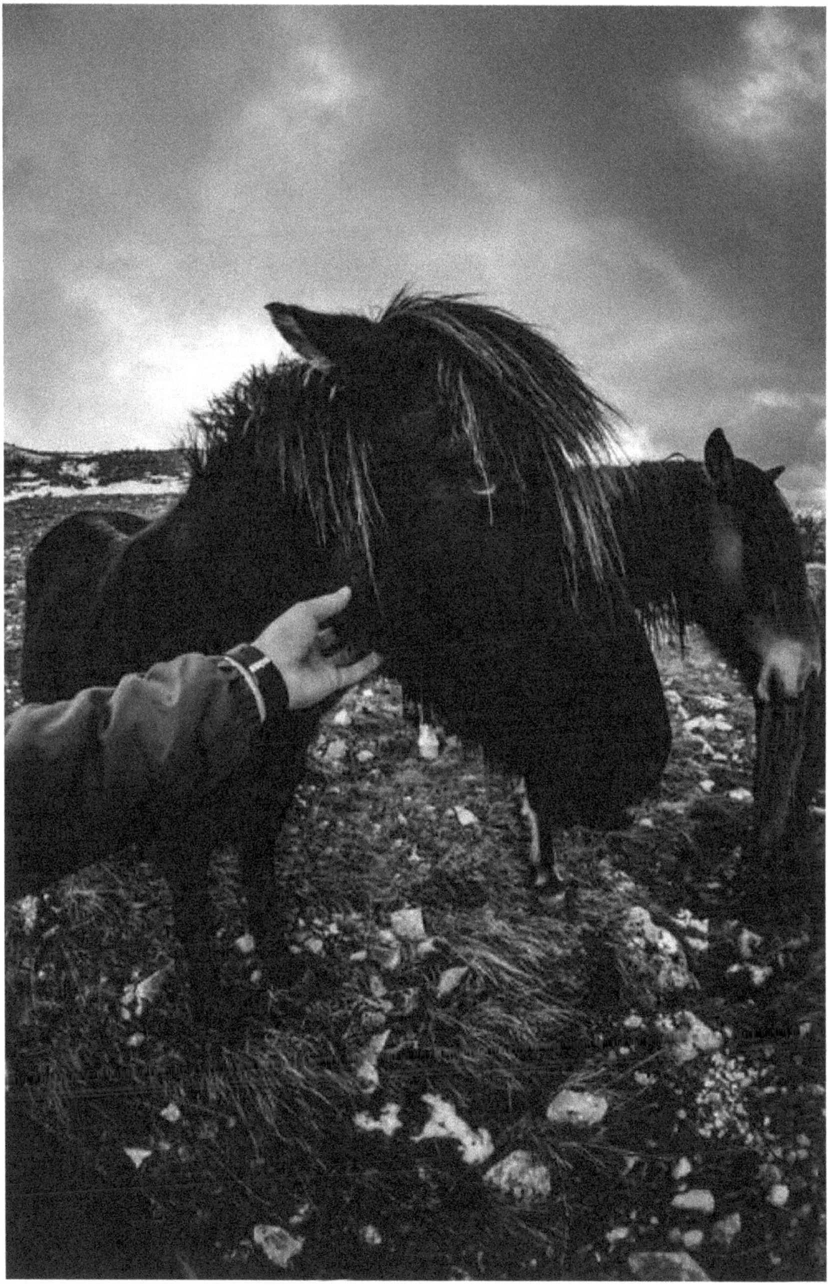

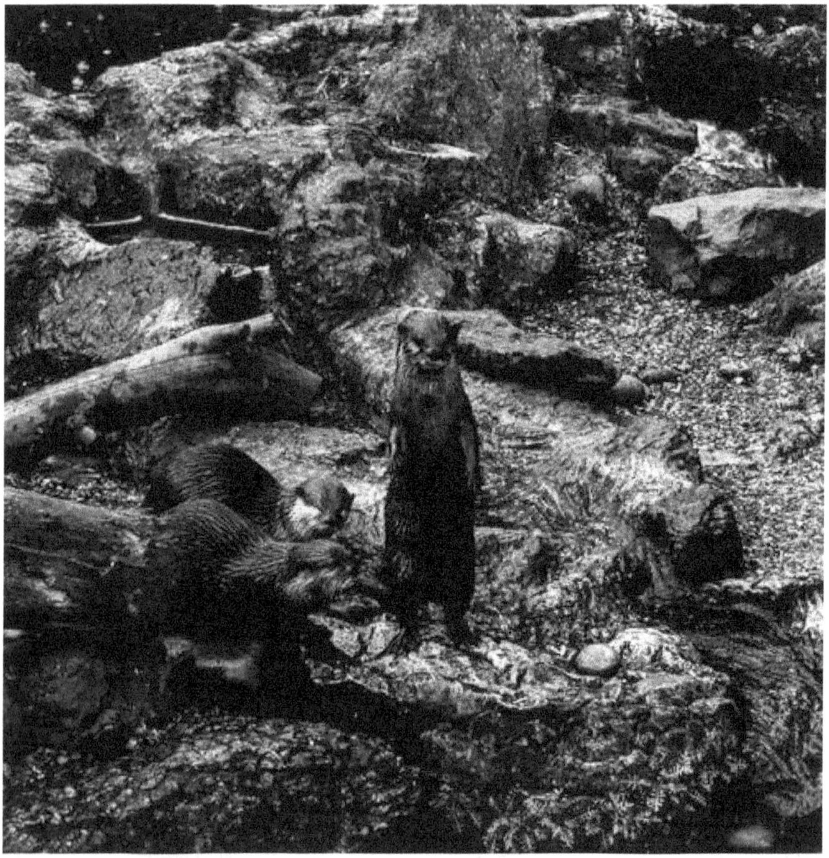

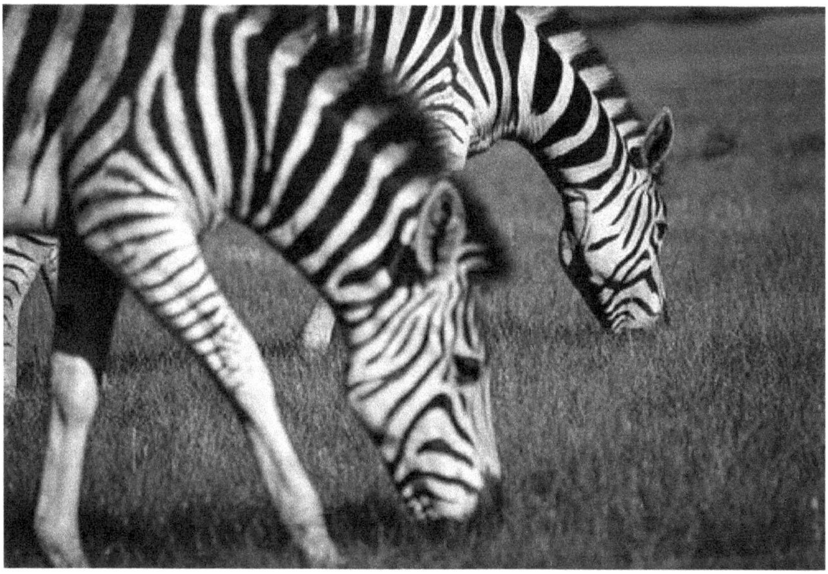

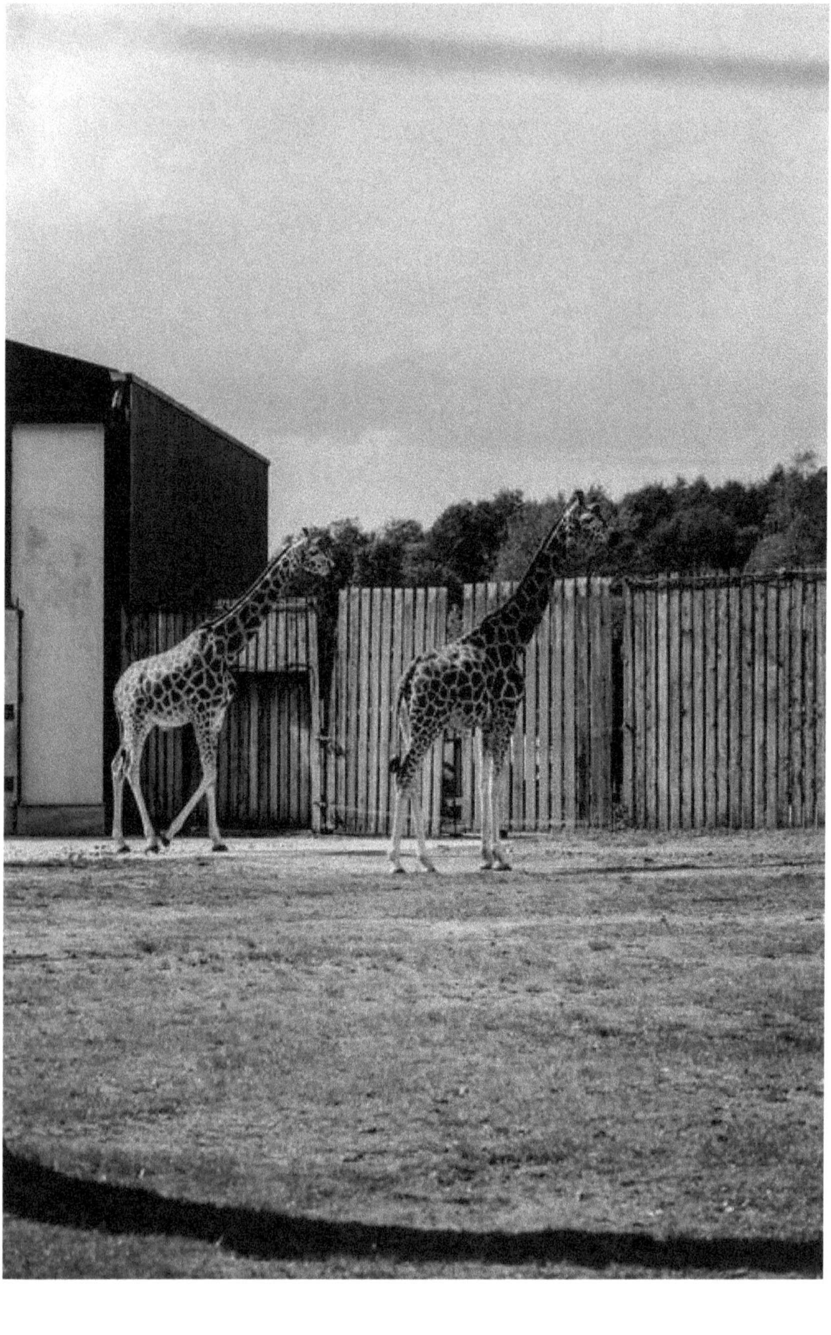

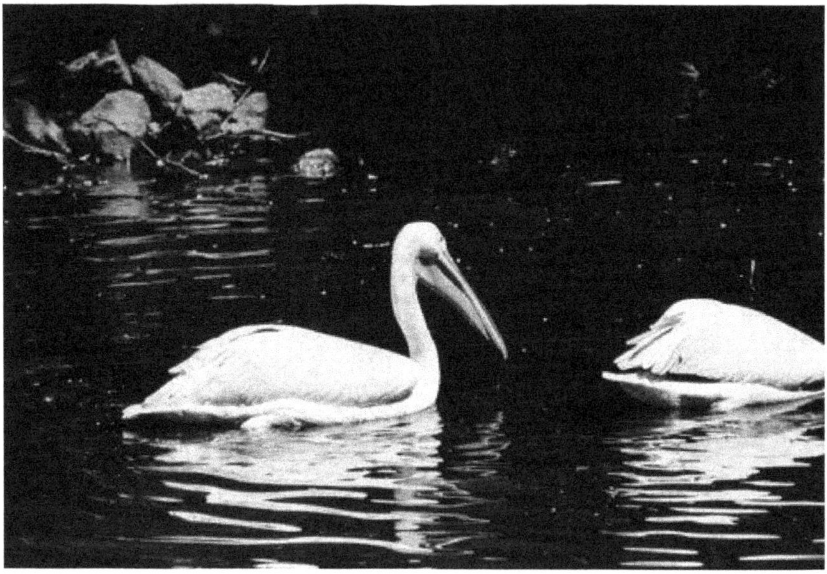

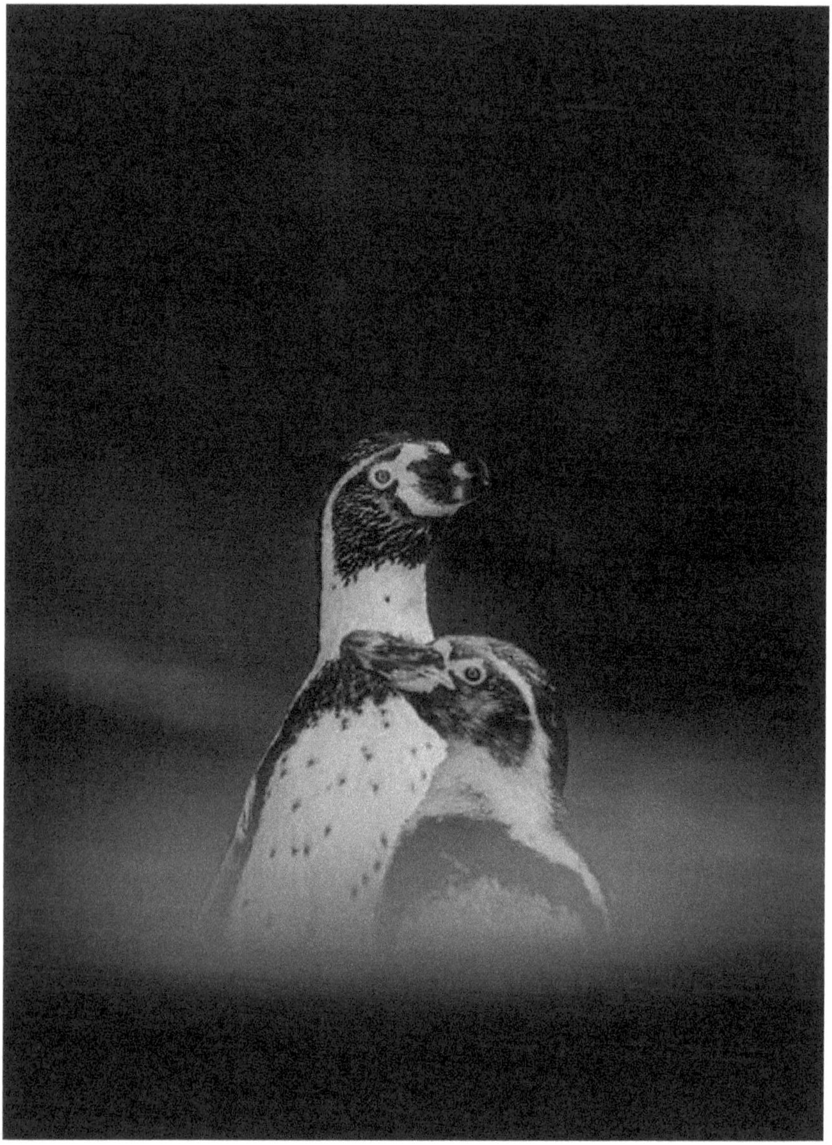

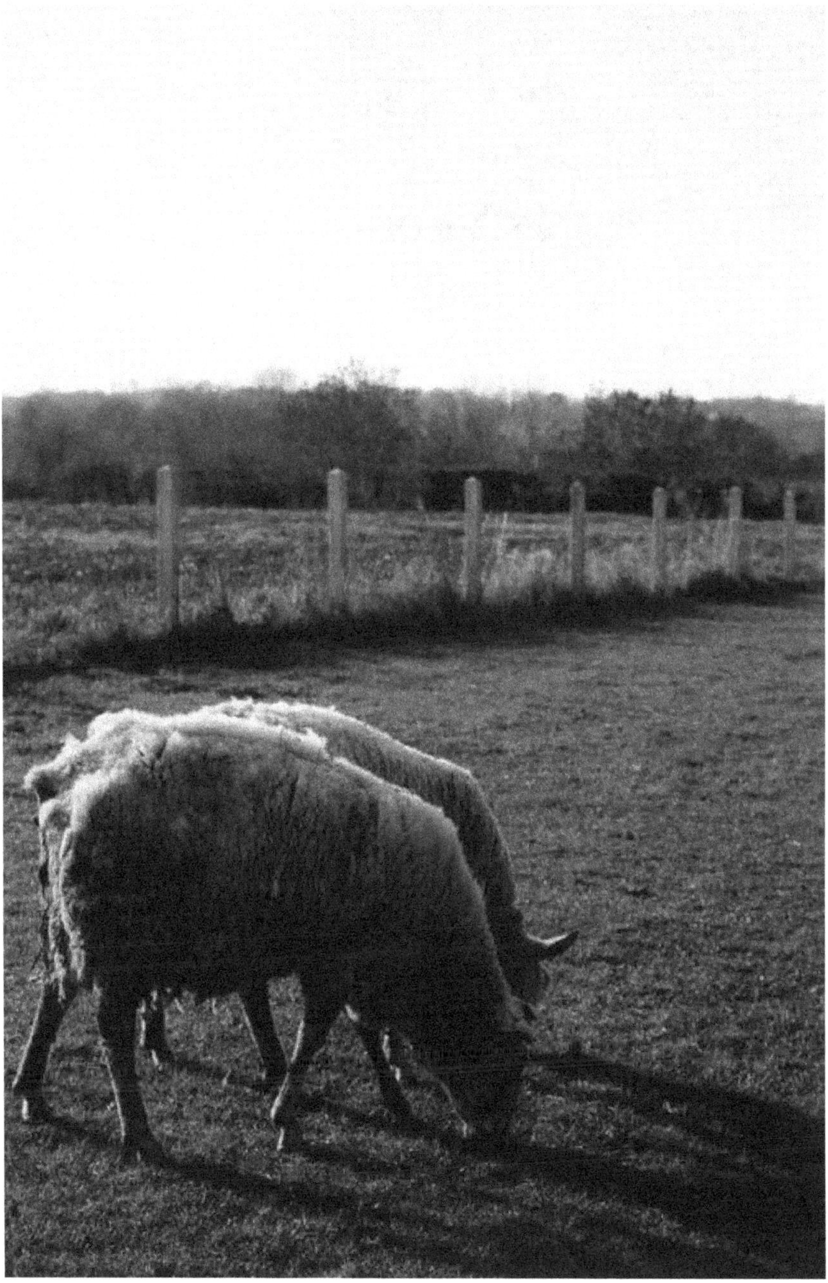

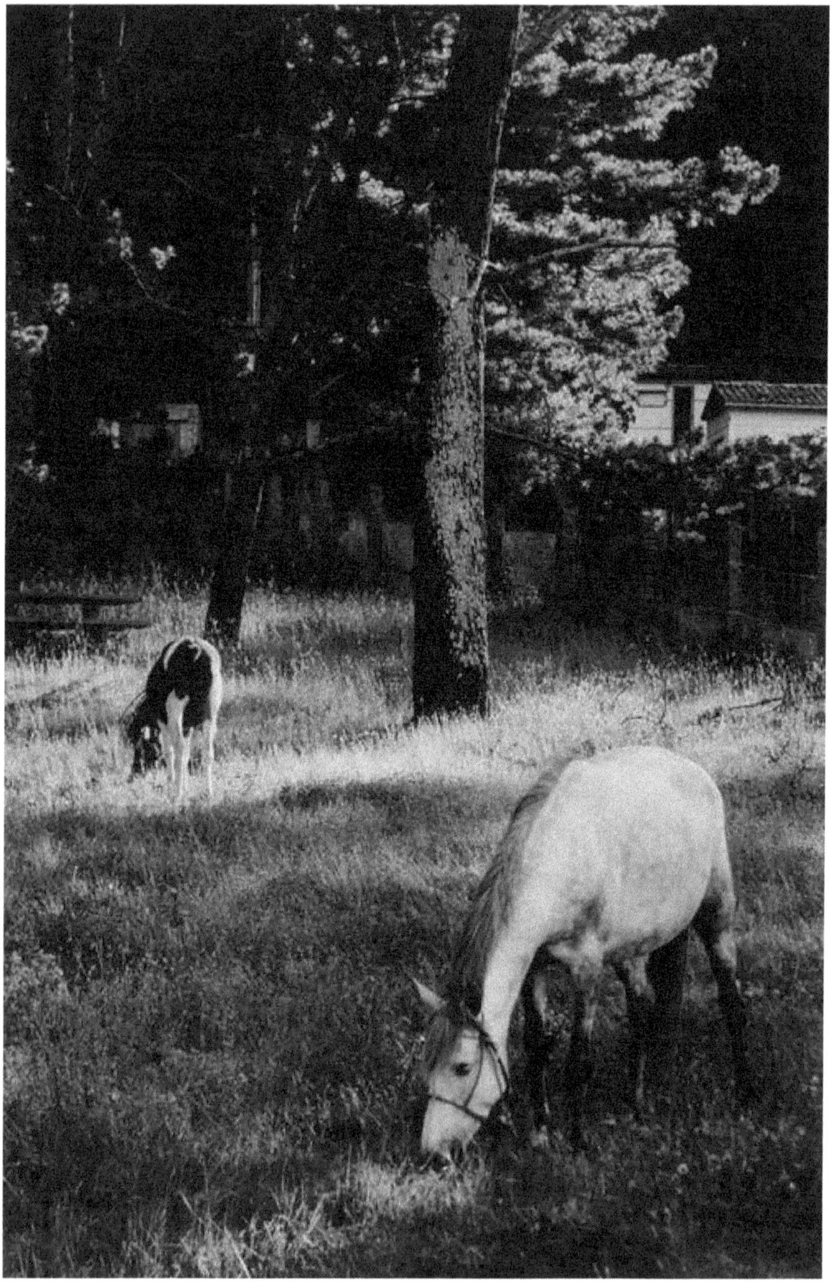

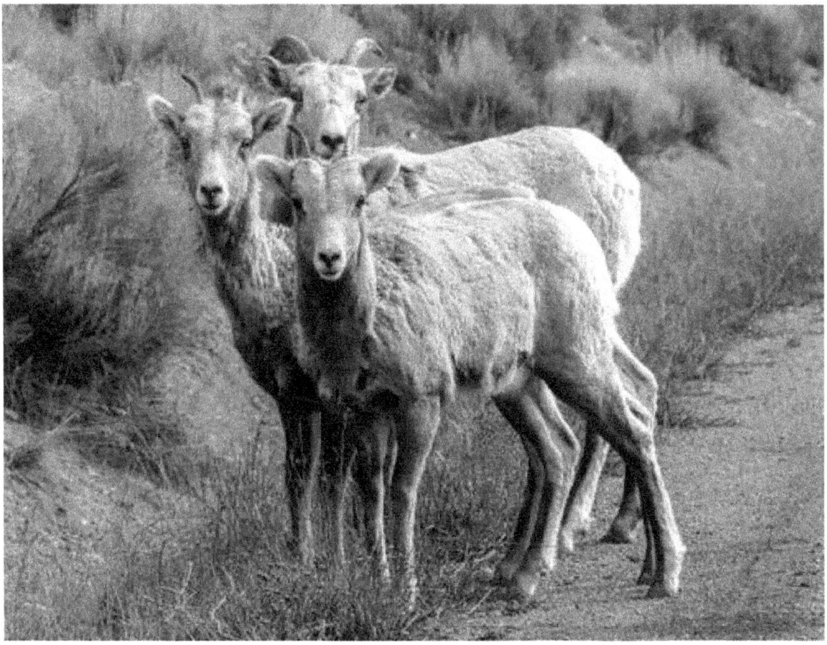

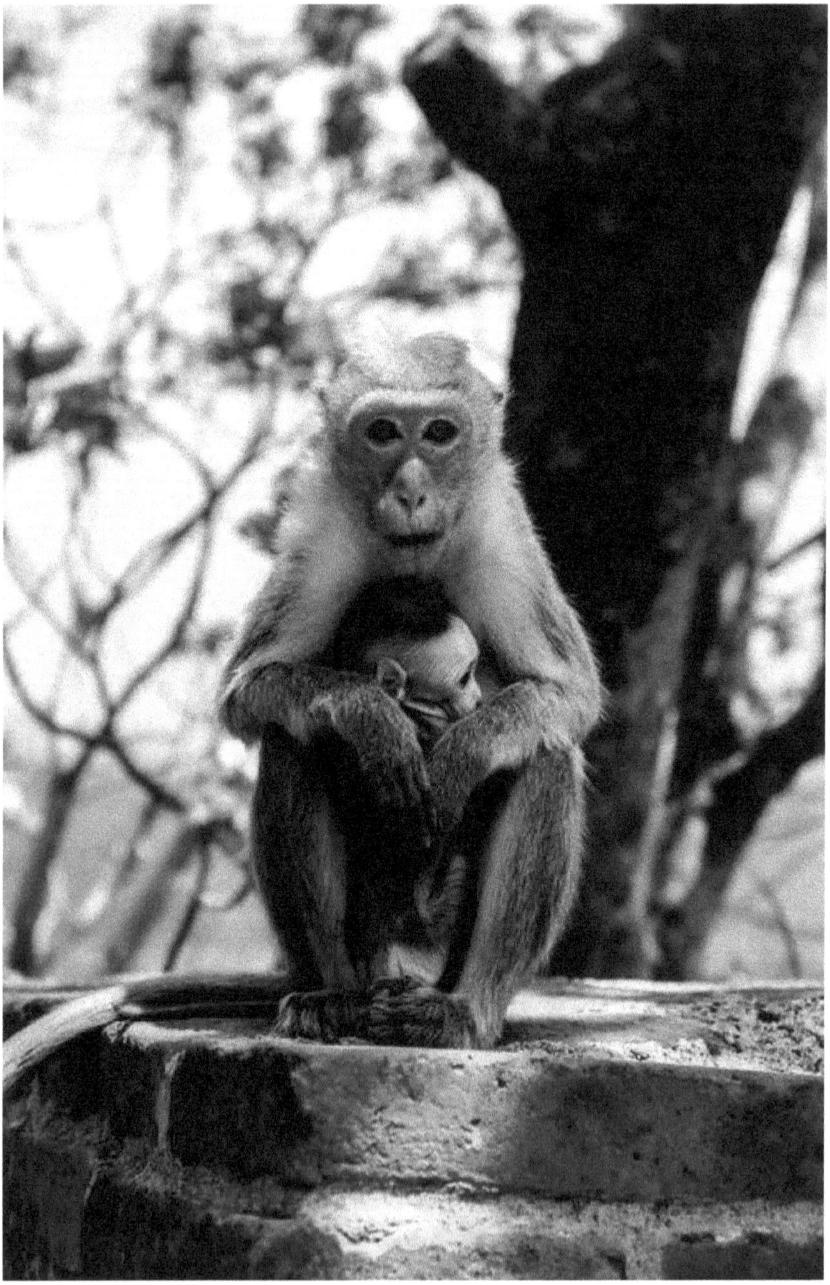

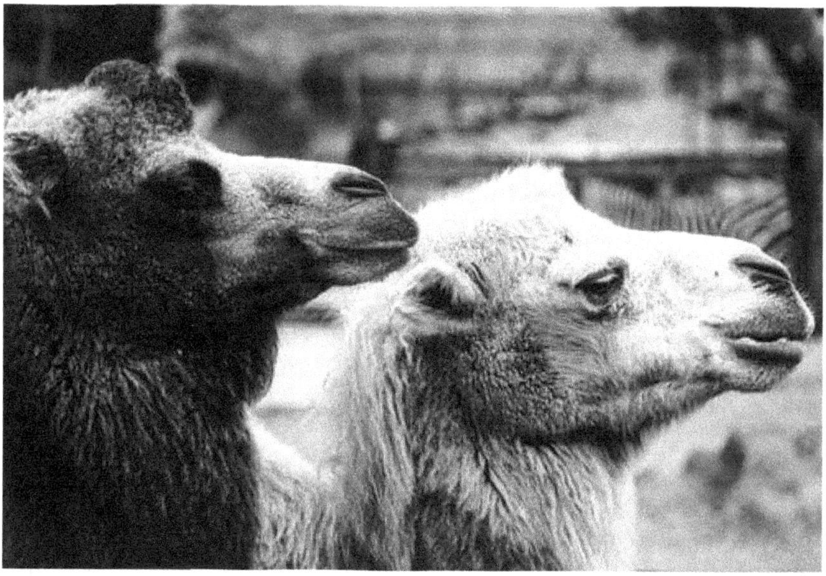

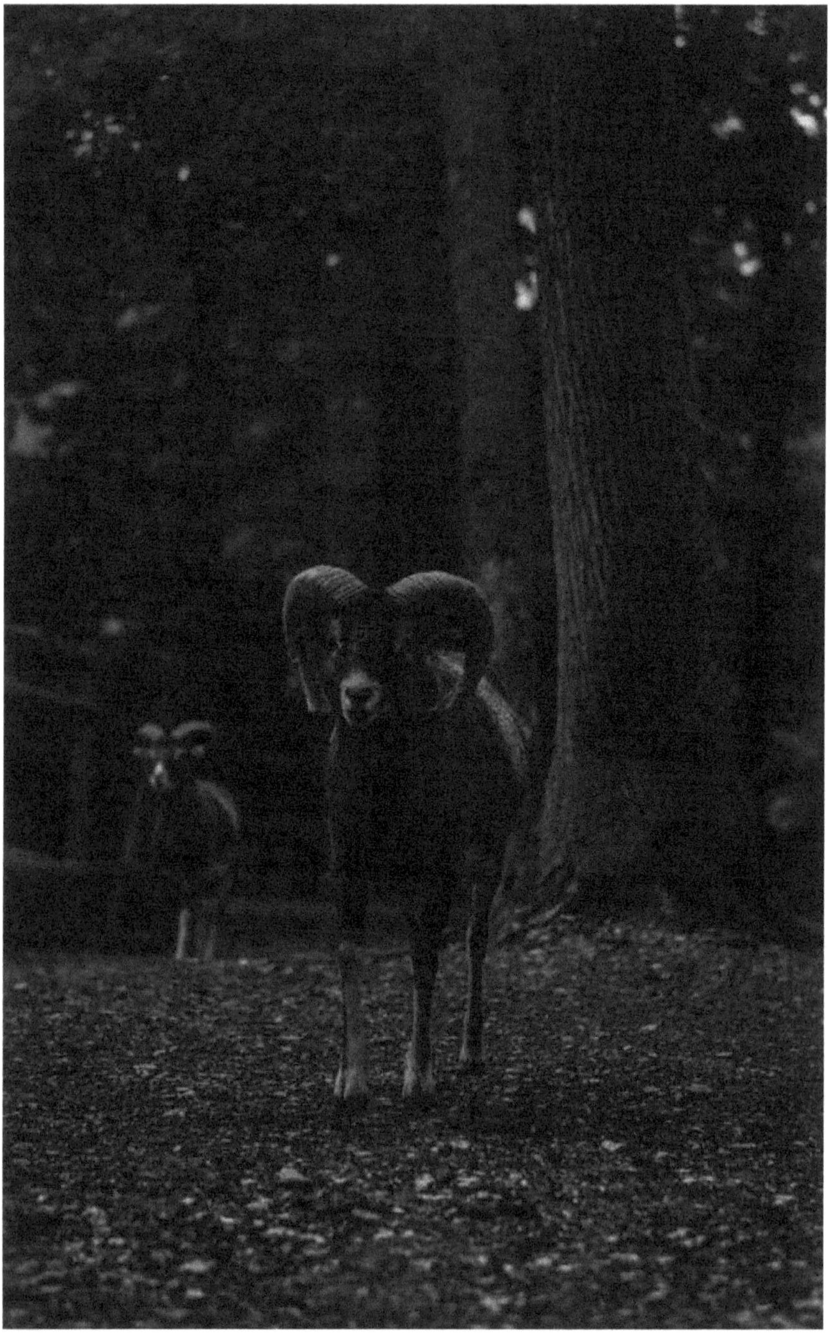

CPSIA information can be obtained
at www.ICGtesting.com
Printed in the USA
BVHW092311210621
610124BV00010B/1989

9 781803 100739